Christmas
&
New years in
Maui 94-95

MOLOKINI

ISLAND

Hawaii's Premier Marine Preserve

by

Mike Severns and Pauline Fiene-Severns

Photographed

by

Mike Severns

This book was made possible by grants from the following sponsors:
Four Seasons Resort Wailea
State of Hawaii Foundation on Culture and the Arts
First Hawaiian Foundation
Frear Eleemosynary Trust
McInerny Foundation
G.N. Wilcox Trust

✦

Molokini - Hawaii's Premier Marine Preserve
© 1993 by Mike Severns and Pauline Fiene-Severns

End papers: *Fungia scutaria* is the largest of the mushroom corals found at Molokini. The mouth is at the center of radiating, grooved septa (dividers) from which tentacles emerge for feeding, usually at night.

First Edition, January 1993

ISBN: 0-9630576-1-8

Underwater photography, Marine Biology, Hawaii

Produced by
Pacific Islands Publishing, Ltd.
430 Hookahi, Suite 23
Wailuku, HI 96793

Printed in Hong Kong

CONTENTS

Photo on front cover:
The endemic darkfin bass, *Holanthias fuscipinnis*, normally lives at depths greater than 400 feet. Prior to this photograph taken at 200 feet, this fish had been seen only through the viewing ports of research submersibles.

At left:
Whale shark, *Rhincodon typus.*
Photo by Rod Canham.

ACKNOWLEDGEMENTS

Many people have helped us in producing this book and deserve special mention.

We are particularly indebted to Dr. John E. Randall, Senior Ichthyologist at the Bernice Pauahi Bishop Museum in Honolulu, who has given freely of his time and technical information throughout.

Our sincere thanks to Stuart Lillico of Oahu for his careful and creative editing; to Dr. E. Alison Kay, Professor of Zoology at the University of Hawaii at Manoa, for her general assistance; to Dr. James E. Maragos, Pacific Protection Planner, The Nature Conservancy, Oahu, for his enthusiastic introduction to corals and for his editorial advice; to Dr. John Sinton, Professor of Geology and Geophysics at the University of Hawaii at Manoa - Hawaii Institute of Geophysics, for explaining some of the geological processes that formed Molokini; to Dr. Terrence M. Gosliner, Chairman of the Department of Invertebrate Zoology at the California Academy of Sciences in San Francisco, for his identification of nudibranchs; to Keali'i Reichel, Director of the Maui Historical Society, for reviewing the Molokini legends; to Richard Pyle of Oahu for his introduction to technical diving which allowed us to dive to the very base of Molokini; to Dave B. Fleetham and Rod Canham of Maui for contributing photographs; to Karin Meier for her boundless enthusiasm and for locating hard to find reference material, and to Janie Culp, John Earle and Teresa Hayes of Oahu for sharing their observations and expertise. Special mention is due Randy Miller of Lahaina for his hours of emergency work on strobes and his genuine interest in maintaining our equipment, and to Rob Larsen and Fox Photo for their generosity in developing thousands of slides.

Support of another nature came from our friends Rod and Ruth Dyerly and Martha and Morgan Hunter, and of course, from our parents, Jim and Roberta Fiene and Ruby Severns. For their encouragement we are sincerely grateful.

This book is dedicated to the memory of my father, Robert L. Severns, who left me a train car in Chicago equivalent in value to the underwater camera equipment necessary to do this book. Without that gift, this book may never have been possible.

Photo at left
Often found on algae-covered objects floating at the ocean's surface is the sea hare *Stylocheilus citrinus*.

FOREWORD

I first dived at Molokini in the early 1970's before it had become a marine sanctuary. I knew within minutes from the exceptional clarity of the sea, the richness of the coral growth, and the diversity of fishes that it would rank among the top dive sites in Hawaii.

My appreciation of Molokini increased when I commenced diving there with Mike and Pauline Severns. Together, we have enjoyed a mutual learning experience: I have helped them with the scientific names of fishes and they have increased my knowledge of the island with discussions of its origin, Hawaiian fishing methods and the lore of the ancient Hawaiians who fished there. With their experienced eye for the rare and unusual, they have taken me to special places to see fishes I particularly wanted to study and capture on film.

The average person who embarks on underwater photography of fishes usually requires a very long time to become proficient. Selecting the correct exposure, framing the subject properly with suitable background, and getting the moving subject in focus requires much practice. It has taken me many years. Mike Severns was an expert within a few months; his photographs of marine life, as one can readily see from the stunning illustrations in this volume, are unexcelled.

Pauline Fiene-Severns makes over 600 dives a year, and is interested in the reproductive cycles of fishes and invertebrates, some of which appear as photos in this book. Her specialty, however, is nudibranchs (had I not been captivated by fishes early on, I am sure that the wildly colorful nudibranchs would have captured my fancy). Her years of searching have yielded hundreds of species, some of them new to science.

When I heard that Molokini had become a marine preserve, I rejoiced. Once fishing, and particularly spearfishing is prevented, populations of the larger fishes increase and the coral reef community regains its proper ecological balance. Fishes soon learn that man is no longer a threat and they can be approached more closely. As word spread of Molokini's excellent snorkeling and diving, visitation became progressively heavier. Damage to the coral from anchoring became a problem. The build up of the stocks of valued sport and food fishes attracted unscrupulous fishermen who could not resist sneaking into the preserve to fish.

Molokini, this jewel set in a deep blue sea, is a treasure for posterity and clearly suffers from a lack of policing. To be fully appreciated, it needs to be fully protected.

– JOHN E. RANDALL

Left:
Portulaca molokiniensis, a recently described plant found on Molokini.

INTRODUCTION

Molokini is perhaps the most unusual of Hawaii's many marine preserves, due to its location and crescent shape. As the only offshore marine preserve in the Hawaiian Islands, it has become one of the most popular diving and snorkeling destinations in the world.

Molokini lies near the southeastern end of the Hawaiian island chain, cradled in the calm, protected waters created by the close proximity of Maui, Lanai, and Kahoolawe. It is one of several crescent-shaped volcanic islands in the Hawaiian chain, but is by far the most accessible, lying only two and three quarter miles off Maui's leeward shore. The island rises 165 feet above sea level at its highest point and is roughly 3,200 feet long and 1,300 feet across from tip to tip.

Resting on the underwater shoulder of Maui, its surrounding 400 to 700 foot deep waters are shallow when compared to the 15,000-foot ocean depth surrounding Hawaii. The ocean bottom at the base of the island's south face is sand and rock, (the talus from the heavily eroded cliffs above), quickly giving way to sand which slopes southward leveling off on a mud and gravel bottom 1,000 feet deep. To the north, facing the West Maui mountains, the bottom drops abruptly to 600 feet before rising gently over several miles into the shallows of Maalaea bay on Maui.

Small when compared to the giant volcanic islands surrounding it, what Molokini lacks in size it makes up for in location. Four of Hawaii's massive volcanic peaks, as well as the islands of Molokai, Lanai, Maui, and Kahoolawe can be seen from Molokini. Its position in the Alalakeiki Channel, separating Maui and Kahoolawe, assures clean, clear water rarely affected by runoff from neighboring islands. Underwater visibility, always good, occasionally approaches two hundred feet.

Above water, the windswept, arid island is tree-less, but enough soil and moisture cling to it to support vegetation on the gentle inner slopes. On the heavily eroded outer wall a few scattered grasses and shrubs persist, and sea birds burrow in crevices to build their nests.

Molokini's crescent shape and offshore location make it ideal for healthy coral reef formation, which provides habitat and shelter for thousands of marine animals. All but a few of Hawaii's coral and reef fish species are represented as well as many pelagic visitors including several whale species, dolphins, monk seals, turtles, whale sharks and, most frequently, manta rays. The marine environment at Molokini provides a superb introduction to the incredible diversity of Hawaiian reef life and to some of the peculiar behavioral characteristics of these animals.

Molokini's marine habitats include the precipitous outer wall, coral reefs, rubble and sand channels of the interior bay. Fishes feed on drifting organisms while hovering over the reefs and along the outer wall where a rainbow of encrusting algae, tunicates and sponges contrasts sharply with the clear deep-blue water of the surrounding ocean.

Though Molokini is one of the tiniest islands in the expansive Hawaiian chain, its spectacular concentration of marine life surpasses most other Hawaiian reefs. Moreover, its inhabitants have become familiar with people as benign creatures, and go about their activities undisturbed. Mating, feeding, territorial displays and species interaction can often be observed from a comparatively short distance. It is no wonder, then, that Molokini has been set aside as a preserve to protect its incredible natural habitats for all to observe and enjoy.

Photo at left
Bubble shell, *Hydatina amplustre*.

11

HISTORY

GEOLOGY

One of East Maui's last fiery exhibitions, the formation of Molokini, produced one of the most spectacular and unusual geologic features in Hawaii. Earth, wind and fire combined forces in the presence of water to form this crescent-shaped island which today harbors a vital array of life. Although man was not here to record the events that took place, the island itself provides us with clues to its past.

Over one million years ago East Maui Volcano began building a base for Molokini on the ocean floor. Then, during a new period of activity tens of thousands of years ago, lava from within the earth was squeezed out through a vent on East Maui's submerged shoulder. This early activity was unapparent above water until the vent opening neared the surface of the ocean. Then, red hot lava contacting the cold, blue water produced violent explosions. Vast amounts of steam blasted the lava into tiny ash particles and propelled a thick black mist of atomized water and ash hundreds of feet into the air. These explosions created consecutive sheets of wet ash dust, each paper thin, which painstakingly built the island 500 feet tall from its underwater base to its top.

Molokini owes its basic shape to the fact that it was an undersea explosion. Ash cones which form on land are relatively high, narrow cones with smaller craters. These form when explosions occur deep within a conduit, or pipe, in the earth, sending the ash straight into the air, where it falls back fairly close to the vent. In contrast, Molokini's very low, wide crater was the result of explosions taking place near the opening of the conduit underwater. When the lava contacted the cold sea water, steam and ash flew out in all directions at a low trajectory, forming a comparatively wide crater, one-half mile in diameter.

Another result of the island's submarine beginnings is its composition of thousands of layers of ash, highly visible along the backside of the island, as well as inside the crater rim and even underwater. Although explosions occurred one after another, enough time passed in between them to create an island made of distinct layers.

Lava and water were not the only factors involved in shaping the volcano. Wind was the force responsible for the island's unusual crescent shape. Although each explosion of ash dust was initially sent upward and outward in all directions, northeasterly tradewinds (which blow from the north at Molokini due to the effects of Maui's landmass) deposited most of the ash downwind, forming a cone higher on one side than the other.

An important part of the island's formation was its transition from an ash cone to a more consolidated tuff cone. The cementation of ash layers is a continuous process which begins soon after eruption, and continues throughout the life of the island. During this process, compounds in the volcanic ash regroup in the presence of water to form a more coherent structure called tuff, which is more resistant to erosion.

When volcanic activity had ceased, the crater rim was a semicircle, smooth inside with a rounded crest and a smooth slope outside. Today Molokini retains only part of that smoothness. Although the inner slopes face windward, they are somewhat protected by Maui and bear a closer resemblance to the island as it looked shortly after formation. Some wind erosion has taken place however, eating away at the weaker layers. When viewed from the right angle, the tougher, more resistant layers stand out as small steps on the inner slopes of the island.

The outer slopes of most of the island are today severe and jagged cliffs. This side, although considered leeward, is the more exposed in terms of wave action because it faces the open ocean. The constant and more erosive work of waves intensifies during storms, typically coming from the south, cutting into the island and undermining the rock above. When this rock loses support, it falls away and over hundreds of years, produces vertical cliffs like those reaching a height of 150 feet along the backside. Exposed cliff faces are then attacked by the wind, the softer parts being removed more readily than the firmer parts, producing an irregular moth-eaten appearance. The original smooth outer layers have been worn away to reveal the strata once hidden inside the island.

A striking effect of erosion is the deep notch cut into the island along the inner and outer shoreline. Below this notch, and a few feet above sea level, is a smooth horizontal surface called a wave bench. Both the notch and the wave bench are the result of waves cutting into the island. Since the backside is exposed to the more formidable southern swells, the wave bench on the back is much more pronounced in places than the bench inside the crater.

Finally, a factor which greatly influenced the island's underwater appearance was the significantly lower sea level present during and following the time of formation. Because the sea level was lower than today, much more of the island was exposed, revealing a crater rim which was roughly three quarters of a circle. At today's sea level, only half a circle is seen above water, but underwater an extension of the western point of the island exists, built of the same numerous layers of ash and showing the same signs of wind and water erosion we see above water. This submerged arm forms a protected bay inside the crater and a substrate on which a variety of corals and other organisms grow.

Another large wave bench, (left), 250 feet below the surface, provides evidence of a time, over 10,000 years ago, when sea level stood about 250 feet lower than it does today. From this we know that Molokini must be at least 10,000 years old.

The final product of the volcanic event we call Molokini will someday be only a small submerged reef, thousands of which are found throughout the Pacific. Until that time, perhaps thousands of years from now, it stands to remind us of Molokini's explosive past.

Photo previous page
Wave bench being cut into the island by wave action.

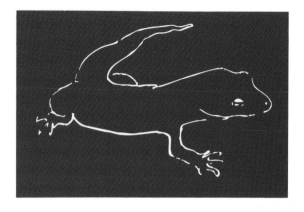

HAWAIIAN LEGENDS

Ki'ina aku Uluhina,
Moku ka piko o ke kamaiki,
Ka 'iewe o ke keiki i lele

I komo i loko o ka 'ape nalu;
Ka 'ape'ape kai 'ale'ale,
Loaa ka malo o ke kama

O Molokini ka moku
He iewe ia -a-,
He iewe ka moku...

Uluhina then was called upon,
The navel of the little one was cut
The afterbirth of the child that was
thrown
Into the folds of the rolling surf,
The froth of the heaving sea,
Then was found the loin cloth for the
child
Molokini the island
is the navel string,
The island is the navel string ...

Abraham Fornander
Collection of Hawaiian Antiquities and Folk-lore Vol. IV

In Hawaiian legends, even small islands such as Molokini are not overlooked. The above verse is from a *mele*, or chant, about the formation and peopling of the main islands as told by a priest of Old Hawaii. In the mele, the island of Hawaii was born to Wakea, the father, and Papa, the mother. Maui was their next offspring, and eleven other islands followed. The island of Kahoolawe, however, was born of different parents, and of a somewhat lower class. When Kahoolawe was born, a very high chief, Uluhina, was called upon to cut the baby's cord, which he threw into the sea along with the afterbirth. Molokini emerged from the sea, formed from the birth cord of Kahoolawe.

The birth of a *mo'o* child begins another legend

describing the origin of Molokini. At that time the islands were inhabited by many supernatural beings, including mo'o. Mo'o were spirits, friendly or unfriendly, that could assume a variety of forms including lizards, monsters, giants, or often beautiful women.

The mo'o mother, Pu'u-o-kali, and mo'o father, Pu'u-hele, had both assumed the shape of hills near what is now Maalaea on the island of Maui. When their first child was born they named her Pu'u-o-inaina and placed her on Kahoolawe, a sacred land at that time. Pu'u-o-inaina became the wife of two brothers and lived with them on Kahoolawe. Eventually there came a time of drought and hunger. In order to grow food and support themselves and their wife, the brothers moved to the West Maui mountain, Hanaula, the only spot where rain continued to fall. Pu'u-o-inaina remained on Kahoolawe and soon took for herself a new husband, Lohi'au. Unfortunately, the handsome Kauai chief was also Pele's husband.

When Pele, Hawaii's fire goddess, arrived on Maui and learned that her husband had become captivated by the beautiful Pu'u-o-inaina she became enraged. The mo'o spirit was cursed by Pele and fled her home in shame, running into the sea. Pele, anxious to see her beloved husband again, waded through the sea in search of him. On her way she found Pu'u-o-inaina in the form of a lizard, her body stretched out from Kahoolawe to Makena. Pele, in jealous anger, slashed the mo'o's body in half, leaving her head as Pu'u-'o-la'i, near Makena, and her tail as the semicircular island of Molokini.

The separation of Molokini from Maui by almost three miles, and Pele's wading through the sea gives a sense of enormity to the legendary confrontation between these two, and to the imagination of the Hawaiian storyteller.

Place names have been derived from other legends as well, with the activities of gods and people giving rise to the names of features of the island. The following is a story explaining several of the place names, as told by the late Inez Ashdown.

During a time when relations between the islands of Hawaii and Maui were friendly a princess from the island of Hawaii was allowed to visit the court of Maui. While there she fell in love with the king of Maui and later became pregnant. The princess, however, was already betrothed to a prince on the island of Hawaii, and it was believed that if she did not honor the betrothal, the two islands would war. To avoid such upheaval the priests of both islands commanded that the unborn child be destroyed. On the princess's return to Hawaii from Maui the *kahuna*, priest, accompanying her stopped at Molokini and took her ashore to carry out his orders to abort the child. His love for the princess and the king was too great, however, and when faced with the task he was unable to obey the command. The name of the ridge along the top of Molokini is called Kahuku, meaning a protuberance, in memory of the enlarging of the princess's body while she carried her unborn child close to the love of her heart. (This child became none other than Kamehameha I, the only Hawaiian ruler to conquer all the main islands and bring them under one rule.)

When the king learned that the priest had disobeyed his orders, he banished the priest to Molokini, and left him alone to die. But the gods of Hawaii are all-knowing, and the kindly priest prayed to his god-spirit, Lono, patron of all growing things, of medicine and of the harvest. Lono heard the prayers of this humble servant and understood. The crescent point on the Maui side of Molokini is today called Pahe'e-o-Lono, meaning the slide of Lono, for it was there that the sacred spear of Lono transformed the compassionate priest into a stone which then slid into the water. And the cove within the crescent arms of Molokini is called Kahulu'ele, swelling billows, after the seas that took the stone priest into their peaceful depths and gave rest and protection to him.

The point of the crescent closest to Kahoolawe is named *Lalilali*, slippery. Formerly known as Lalelale, it was a place where priests came to pray. The origins of other place names may or may not be directly tied to particular legends, but that is difficult to ascertain since few written legends exist about Molokini.

HISTORY
OF THE ISLAND

HAWAIIANS AND MOLOKINI

Hawaiians have no doubt been visiting Molokini for as long as they have lived along the neighboring shores of Maui. Villagers from the nearby coast would not have found it difficult to hunt and capture birds attracted to the isolated island, and gather the eggs during the March-to-August nesting period. The island may also have been used for layovers during trips between Kahoolawe and Maui, or as an overnight refuge for fishermen from nearby villages.

Year-round fishing was probably the most common activity at Molokini. Nets of *olona,* a natural nylon-like fiber, weighted with small, carved stones were laid in shallow water along Molokini's inner bay. *Wili wili,* a buoyant wood, *Erythrina sandwicensis,* was attached at the top as a float to hold the nets up. Carved net sinkers, probably lost at the bottom due to tangled nets, have been recovered recently.

Octopus were caught with a *luhe'e,* a fishing lure, dragged or bounced slowly along the bottom from a canoe. Since the octopus has excellent eyesight and is a tenacious predator, this method of fishing was very rewarding. Hawaiians called it an *ipo,* lover, referring to the embrace of the octopus on the deadly lure.

The bait of the octopus lure was a large cowry shell lashed to a *pohaku luhe'e,* coffee bean-shape stone sinker with a carved groove to hold the line. A wooden stick which formed the hook shank was sandwiched between the sinker and the shell bait, leaving several inches of wood extending from either end of the lure. The fisherman tied his line to one end of the shank and fastened a wooden barb with the point curving toward the cowry-shell lure at the other. Strips of *kapa,* bark cloth, were often tied behind the hook, forming what modern fishermen call a skirt. When the fisherman felt an octopus embrace the lure, he would yank the cord, hooking the animal, quickly bringing it to the surface. Several carved sinkers of this type were found in shallow water at Molokini after a severe storm in 1980.

In deeper water outside the crater, small, uncarved, beachworn stones litter the bottom. Geologically unrelated to Molokini, they were brought to the island by Hawaiian fishermen, usually as sinkers in *palu* fishing. Palu was a paste made from unappetizing fish parts for use as chum. Wrapped in kapa with a smooth stone a few inches in diameter, the palu was lowered on the fishing line. When the fisherman felt his line touch the bottom, he gave it a jerk and the stone fell away, spilling the palu from its kapa wrapping. Drifting down-current, the scent of chum enticed fish to the baited hooks. Palu stones litter the bottom in areas where the fishing was good.

The strong current that often sweeps past Molokini required special tackle to fish the deeper outer ledges. Some fishermen used a large teardrop-shaped stone that offered less resistance to the rushing water, allowing them to lower their lines without having them swept back toward the surface by the current. These sinkers were meticulously carved, swollen at the bottom and tapering at the top to a small knob around which the fishing line was secured. Weighing as much as five pounds, they have been found as deep as 180 feet. Larger smooth stones, are common in shallower water and may have been used as canoe anchors, as similar stones are used today throughout Polynesia.

Except for stone sinkers and anchors there is little evidence of early Hawaiian activity at Molokini. Everything else - wood and bone fishhooks, *olona* cord, and shell lures - has disappeared.

WESTERN HISTORY

Molokini's existence was not known to Europeans until the closing years of the eighteenth century. The British navigator and explorer Captain James Cook, on H.M.S. *Resolution*, sighted and charted some of the Hawaiian Islands in 1774 and 1775. French explorer Jean-Francoise de Galoup, Compte de La Perouse, however, actually sighted Molokini and charted its location in 1786. In 1793 British Captain George Vancouver charted Molokini and finally offered the first description, a "barren and uninhabited islet".

In 1883, King David Kalakaua hired two American engineers, E.D. Baldwin and Arthur C. Alexander, to survey the island. Shortly thereafter Molokini was officially included in the charted Hawaiian Islands.

The first scientific survey was conducted in February, 1913 by botanist C.N. Forbes, who recorded a total of fifteen plant species. During a 1925 geologic survey by H.S. Palmer, in which he mapped the island and its underwater contours, he collected a sampling of plants from which E.L. Caum identified seven additional species. A 1980 reconnaissance by Gar Clarke added twelve more, and recent visits by Robert Hobdy have brought the total number to 56 species, of which about 62% are non-native.

A species of succulent, collected during each of these surveys, was confirmed as a new species in 1987 by Robert Hobdy. Known only from the arid islands of Molokini, Kahoolawe and the island of Puu Koae off Kahoolawe, the species was named *Portulaca molokiniensis.*

Molokini's position in the middle of the Alalakeiki Channel made a lighthouse essential and the first was erected in 1911. During World War II, however, the light was extinguished and the island was used to train bombardiers. In 1947, when target practice ended, a new wooden tower was constructed which stood for forty-two years. It was replaced by a permanent stainless steel lighthouse.

From the late 1950's through the 1970's, black coral was harvested commercially from deep water. Today, little black coral remains, a stark contrast to descriptions from former black coral divers who told of huge trees in dense stands along the outer wall of the island. Many stumps remain, attesting to the once prolific black coral population.

As recreational use of the island increased, concern arose over unexploded ordnance left inside the crater from years of U.S. target practice. The U.S. Navy responded by detonating two large bombs in 1975 near spectacular coral, devastating the area. A Navy threat to detonate more bombs in 1984 was forestalled by local divers who dragged the bombs into deep water. In spite of this successful, though dangerous act, more Navy bomb detonations occurred later that year in coral gardens once described as the most beautiful in the state. After much public outcry, the Navy removed several bombs in 1988 and dropped them in 1000 foot waters, miles from Molokini.

Since 1978 Molokini has been a State-managed seabird sanctuary. The Hawaiian Audubon Society in 1980 listed only two species of birds breeding on the island. Roosting or feeding species brought the total to eight. The society estimated that as many as 1500 pairs of birds nest on the island, the overwhelming majority being Wedge-tailed Shearwaters, *Puffinus pacificus.*

Recognition of the island's exploitation came in 1977 when the State of Hawai'i officially declared Molokini and its surrounding waters a Marine Life Conservation District. It is now illegal to bottomfish, spearfish, or remove anything naturally occurring, living or dead, down to a depth of 180 feet. Moorings have been placed within the crater to help stop destruction to the fragile coral by anchors, and plans for further protection are underway.

Photo above left: A carved Hawaiian octopus lure sinker stone photographed as it was found on the bottom in 1983.

SAND

S A N D

Of the different underwater habitats at Molokini, sand is probably the most overlooked and least understood. A complex world all its own, most of the inhabitants are hidden from view, living buried in the sand, while others expose themselves only at night in search of food. Often underestimated in its contribution to the richness of marine life, sand harbors some of the island's most fascinating animals.

When Molokini was newly-formed there was no sand habitat available for potential sand inhabitants. Slowly, the processes by which sand is formed began to take place. Erosion of the island by wind and waves was first to occur, forming comparatively dark volcanic sand. Gradually, however, the disintegration of the skeletons of tiny animals (foraminifera, mollusks, echinoderms, corals, etc.) began, and over time contributed the greater part of the island's sand, which is now almost white. Due to Molokini's isolation, analysis of the composition of the island's sand is good evidence of the types of animals that inhabit the crater.

Very slowly sand particles settled to the bottom, filtering down through coral, rubble and rock until they began to accumulate in areas where they could fall no further. The accumulations formed low sand channels which alternate with extensive high coral beds. This sand flows imperceptibly out of the mouth of the crater to the deeper water beyond the reef. Sand channels are found throughout the crater and break up an otherwise uninterrupted garden of coral.

As sand habitat formed, it attracted animals with the special adaptations necessary for life in the sand. Algae might have been first to find suitable habitat, followed by worms and worm-eating animals such as mollusks. While pioneering organisms were colonizing the sand, fishes, echinoderms and crustaceans, which feed on these organisms, were attracted in increasing numbers.

The abundance of food offered by sand makes it a

prime place for many animals to live in or near. The most common adaptation of animals able to survive in this habitat, is the ability to live buried underneath the sand. Some animals, such as worms and mollusks, may live deep in the sand, while others such as crabs, starfishes and eels may live just beneath the surface. Fishes such as wrasses and gobies may dive into it for temporary protection or even retire into it for the night.

Another common adaptation is camouflage. Flatfishes, which have a body configuration adaptive for living on the sea floor, assume cryptic coloration and often toss sand on top of themselves to perfectly blend with the sandy bottom. Some eels live buried in the sand with only their heads exposed. The head coloration is mottled and blends with nearby rubble or sponge. Other fishes, such as lizardfishes or gobies, possess bland coloration which serves them well in the sand. A few animals, such as octopuses, will assume a lighter color when crossing sandy areas while traveling or feeding, as will goatfishes, flounders, lizardfishes and others.

An aerial view shows a pattern of sand channels winding throughout the crater and eventually exiting through the mouth of the bay. Some of these channels extend down to the ocean floor facilitating the introduction of unusual animals which normally live on sand in very deep water. These steeply sloping channels are unique in this respect, offering a rare opportunity to view several deep-dwelling echinoderms and some sand-burrowing wrasses which have followed these pathways of sand into relatively shallow water.

The winding sand channels within the crater reflect sunlight, adding remarkable color and excitement to the preserve. They are both pathways and vital habitats which greatly enrich the variety of life at Molokini.

Pages 20 - 21
The robust Hawaiian sea star, *Pentaceraster hawaiiensis,* ranging in color from purple to yellow, occasionally moves up the sand channels from deep water, but never stays long.

Left
The contrasting colors of the firefish, *Nemateleotris magnifica*, help it
blend with rubble and sand. Goatfishes often chase firefish into hiding,
then search for them in the sand with their barbel "whiskers."

Above
Young octopuses often hide in the sand during the day, occasionally coming out to feed. This young *Octopus cyanea* may be hunting for small crabs
among empty helmet-shell egg cases.

Below
If attacked, this golden sea cucumber, an undescribed species of *Bohadschia*, will eject a mass of white strands, "Cuverian organs," that stick to the attacker and, in the case of a crab, may immobilize it completely.

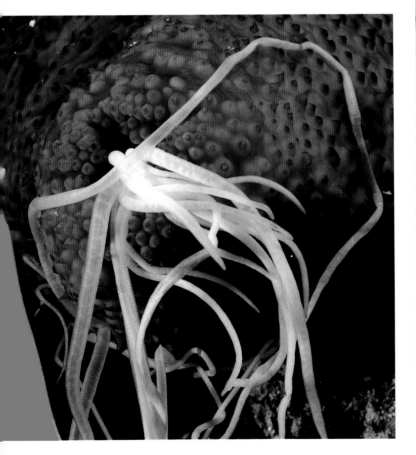

Left

The face of *Ophichthus erabo* is so inoffensive that the animal's predatory nature escapes the casual observer. This eel lies buried in the sand with just its head exposed and little is known of its habits.

Below

This spotted conger eel, *Poeciloconger fasciatus*, was the sixth specimen of the species on record. Previously, one had been recorded from Madagascar, one from Tahiti, one from Indonesia and two from Hawaii. *P. fasciatus* feeds at night and spends the day in a burrow with just the top of its spotted head exposed.

Below
A manybar goatfish, *Parupeneus multifasciatus*, swims with a school of raccoon butterflyfish, *Chaetodon lunula*, to take advantage of the school's ability to disrupt the natural order and increase the goatfish's chance of catching a meal.

Left bottom
Fine sand clings to the mucus coating of the sea cucumber *Holothuria atra*. The weight of the sand may cause some of its mucus coating to sag and fall away.

Above
Parrotfishes, such as this palenose parrotfish, *Scarus psittacus*, often sleep along the edges of the sand channels at night.

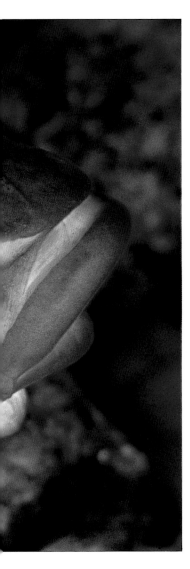

Left

The blue goatfish, *Parupeneus cyclostomus*, is a formidable hunter, using its long, powerful barbels to search beneath rocks and sand. These robust fish hunt in packs that often include a small jack whose superior speed allows it to snatch flushed prey from the goatfish.

Bottom Left

The dragon wrasse — actually a juvenile rockmover, *Novaculichthys taeniourus* — drifts listlessly a few inches above the bottom like a piece of seaweed. When threatened, it can fold its delicate fins and vanish instantly into the sand.

Below

Possessing a venomous defense in its spines, the sea urchin, *Astropyga radiata,* usually inhabits deep water, but occasionally follows a sand channel up into the shallower water of the crater.

Above
The skeleton of the thornback cowfish, *Lactoria fornasini*, is composed of polygonal bone plates that interlock to form a "coat of armor" just beneath the skin, allowing only the eyes, fins and mouth to move.

Right
The male (far right) and female (right) of this endemic wrasse, *Coris ballieui*, are so different that they were originally accepted as separate species — *C. ballieui* for the male and *C. rosea* for the female.

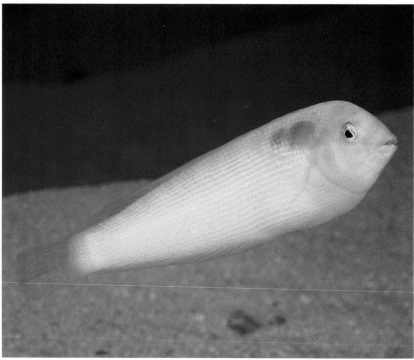

Above

Stegopontonia commensalis is well adapted to life on a black sea urchin whose long spines provide protection and match the shrimp's color pattern. It is unusual to find this dark commensal shrimp on the blond *Astropyga radiata.*

Above
A humpback whale, *Megaptera novaean-gliae*, over one of the sand channels inside the crater.

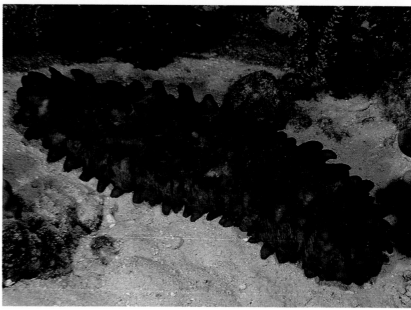

Left

The large *Stichopus horrens*, like other sea cucumbers, ingests large quantities of sand for the microscopic organisms mixed in it. Undisturbed, its movements are slow and graceful, but when bothered it suddenly becomes rigid by tightly interlocking the spicules within its skin. Many species of sea cucumbers are hosts to symbionts (unrelated, but often beneficial species). Among these, the most beautiful is the imperial shrimp, *Periclimenes imperator* (above) which feeds on small organisms and parasites that cling to the slow-moving host. Eggs can be seen on the abdomen of the female.The most bizarre passenger on *S. horrens* is a pearl fish, *Carapus mourlani.* (right) When foraging, it roams the back of its host into whose anus it retreats when threatened.

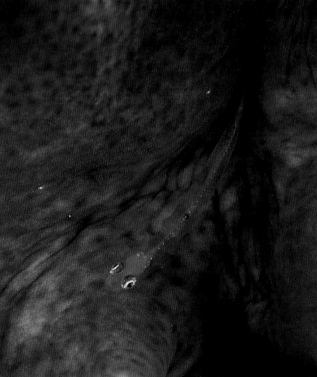

Above

Tentacles of the brown anemone, *Aiptasia pulchella*, capture small prey
and bits of drifting organic material, then pass them to the mouth. Despite
its apparent immobility, the brown anemone rarely remains in one place
more than a couple of days.

Above right

The squid, *Sepioteuthis lessoniana*, may be a common species at Molokini, but because of its nocturnal habits it is almost never encountered. When disturbed, it jets off quickly leaving in its place a dark cloud of ink which creates a diversion, aiding the squid's escape.

Right

At night, harp shells, such as this *Harpa major*, emerge from beneath the sand to feed on crabs and shrimps. Just after this photo was taken, the harp shell suddenly thrust out its mantle, engulfing an inch-long hermit crab which had left the protection of its shell, presumably to make a more quick (but unsuccessful) retreat.

Left

Poised at the entrance to its burrow, this mantis shrimp is hardly noticeable. Rising stealthily as prey nears, and arching its back in a long slim curve, with lightning speed it impales its prey on long barbs on the mantislike forearms. In a world where fishes commonly prey on shrimps, the mantis shrimp feeds primarily on fishes.

Below left

At dawn, when a calm sea preserves patterns in the sand left by activities of the night before, the ten-ray outline of the giant *Luidia* sun star is visible. Sometimes nearby are the remains of a sea mouse or sea cucumber consumed during the night. This nocturnal predator feeds by extruding its stomach, digesting the prey while holding it with tube feet.

Top

The crocodile eel, *Brachysomophis henshawi*, is well adapted to hunting in sand. Its eyes are far forward on its snout, so exposure above the sand is minimal and the fleshy fringe of the mouth filters sand from the water when the eel "breathes." Just behind the eyes, the head swells abruptly with powerful jaw muscles, then gradually tapers along a finless body to a hard, pointed tail for burrowing.

Bottom

A crocodile eel, *Brachysomophis henshawi*, has attacked a pinktail triggerfish, *Melichthys vidua*, and dragged it beneath the sand. The eel had lain in wait in the same place for several days. After it had fed, it moved to a new location.

Left

The iridescence of Wood's razor wrasse, *Novaculops woodi*, glows under the camera's strobe light. Unlike most razor wrasses, *N. woodi* will swim several feet above the bottom in its search for food.

Top

These two spotted goatfish, *Parupeneus pleurostigma*, were seen resting in the same place for several days perhaps because the fish in the background had an injury near its tail. When disturbed, they would swim away together a short distance, then return.

Right

Isolated rocks offer Schauinsland's sand perch, *Parapercis schauinslandi*, a good vantage point as well as shelter. Clouds of minute shrimplike mysids which hover above the sand are frequently the prey.

Something of an enigma is *Xyrichtys pavo* (right), a large, sand-burrowing wrasse. While photographing for this book the authors noted a fish that appeared to be changing from light to dark. It has been suggested that *X. niger (far right)* may be a black phase of *X. pavo* (pers. communication - John Earle). Juvenile *X. pavo* (above) differ remarkably from the adult form.

Above

Of the many species of flatfishes in Hawaiian waters, *Bothus mancus*, the manyray flatfish, is probably the most common at Molokini. It roams the sand channels and coral rubble, feeding on small fishes and crustaceans.

Left

Rarely seen, the deep-dwelling black razor wrasse, *Xyrichtys niger*, spends its days searching the sand channels looking for signs that will lead it to a meal. It is quick to run from intruders.

Above

Goatfishes such as this Pfluger's goatfish, *Mulloidichthys pflugeri*, locate
food with chemosensory organs in the fleshy barbels beneath their chin.
A quick thrust of the snout deep into the sand snares the buried meal.
The sand is then "blown" through the gills, leaving the prey to be swallowed.

Above
The flying gurnard, *Dactyloptena orientalis*, "walks" the sand bottom on its pelvic fins to flush small flatfishes from the sand, then chase and eat them. When threatened, this gurnard spreads its oversize pectoral fins like two elegant fans, confusing the predator with its dramatic increase in size.

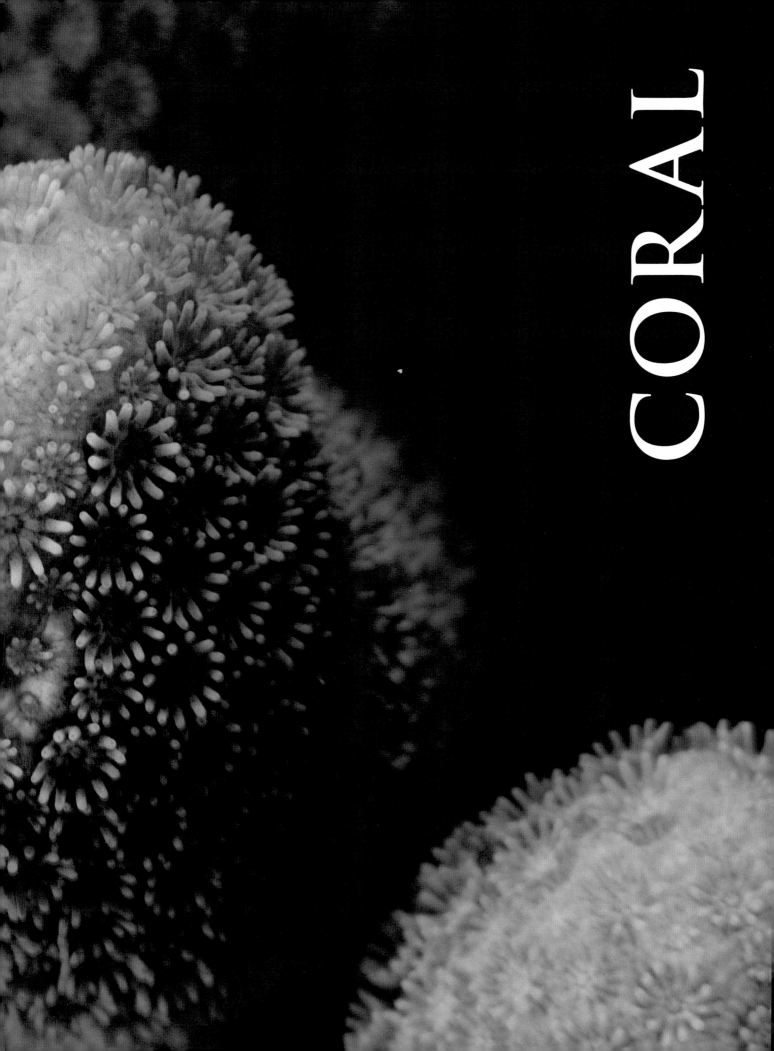

CORAL

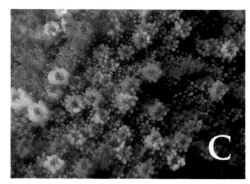

CORAL REEF

olokini presents a virtual wonderland for coral observation due to the exceptional variety, abundance, and coverage of corals. Well over half of the reef-building species found in Hawaii occur at Molokini, making it one of Hawaii's most prolific and spectacular coral gardens.

Hawaii's great distance from the western Pacific, where many species of corals originated, has limited the number of coral species reaching Hawaiian waters. In addition, Hawaii's position at the northern edge of the tropics has resulted in less-than-favorable environmental conditions. Subtropical water temperatures and less intense light levels limit coral colonization and growth. In spite of this, Hawaii has beautiful coral growth, even by world standards.

Corals are dispersed through their eggs and larvae which drift as part of the plankton in ocean currents. After a period of time, which differs from species to species, the larvae settle to the bottom, and those that find hospitable habitat mature. Once attached to a substrate, the larva develops into a polyp and secretes a hard skeleton of calcium carbonate. If it is a colonial species its polyps begin to divide, forming a colony.

A coral colony consists of many hard, cup-like structures of calcium carbonate, each of which supports a living animal, or polyp. Most species of corals expand their polyps mainly at night for feeding. When expanded, each polyp has a peripheral ring of tentacles containing stinging cells which capture and kill small animals of the zooplankton, then pass them to the central mouth to be eaten. Since the polyps are connected by living coral tissue, the entire colony benefits from the catch of one polyp.

Corals are not alone in the reef-building process. Algae called zooxanthellae live protected in the tissue of reef-building corals, removing the carbon-dioxide waste of the coral's respiration system. This aids the coral animal in depositing its calcium carbonate skeleton. During the day the zooxanthellae utilize the carbon-dioxide in photosynthesis, the by-products of which provide the coral with food and oxygen. In turn, the wastes of the coral serve as nutrients for the algae. Other organisms, especially encrusting coralline algae, add to the mass of the reef by cementing coral skeletons together forming a strong, solid reef.

Molokini's unique location and its configuration of steep outer slopes and protected inner bay, provides the necessary conditions for healthy coral growth. The island's off-shore location and clear water facilitate excellent light penetration allowing exceptional deep water coral growth. Also, its location in the 'Alalakeiki Channel subjects it to moderate current and surge, which further stimulates coral growth.

A close look at Molokini's coral population adds another dimension to the island's spectacular diversity of life. Different areas of the crater foster different formations and combinations of corals that can be divided into three zones. Each zone reflects a different set of conditions such as amount of light, depth, surge, competition from other corals and predation by other animals.

The first zone, the submerged arm of the crater rim and the shallow coastal waters of the inner bay, has one of the highest diversities of coral species, among shallow coral habitats, in Hawaii. Corals which require intense light penetration and can tolerate occasional scouring wave action thrive here. The dominant species in this habitat is the rose coral, *Pocillopora meandrina*, joined by antler coral, *Pocillopora eydouxi* and small colonies of lobe coral, *Porites lobata*. These corals are variable in color depending on their zooxanthellae, creating an array of pastels enhanced by the bright sunlight.

A second zone, the intermediate reef, is found in deeper water inside the protected bay of the crater, and has more lush and complex coral growth than the shallow coral community. A similar number of species is present, but the particular species differ. Another striking difference is the sheer bulk of the coral in the intermediate reef. More successful species have overgrown other species, building impressive formations on top of one another without the threat of rough water to knock them down. These dense mounds of coral stand many feet higher than the low sand channels bordering them, emphasizing their great mass.

Competition among corals is a constant process and can be readily observed in the intermediate reef. Two encrusting corals, *Montipora capitata* and *Montipora patula* repeatedly overgrow other corals such as the finger coral, *Porites compressa*, and lobe coral, *Porites lobata*, the vertical growth forms of which are not always fast enough to avoid coverage by other corals. The co-dominance of these two *Montipora* species is an unusual combination not reported anywhere else in Hawaii.

Although apparently the more successful coral at Molokini in terms of coverage, *Montipora* species are also among the favored foods of the crown-of-thorns starfish, *Acanthaster planci*. Effects of crown-of-thorns feeding can be seen occasionally among living colonies. The starfish may digest the external living tissues of an entire coral colony, leaving only the stark, white skeleton. The dead coral surface, while unsightly, is then open for re-colonization by algae, corals and other organisms. Complete recovery may take many years if major sections of the reef have been killed off.

The third zone is the deep reef, characterized by very clear water, steep slopes and reduced light. Coral growth at depths of 100 feet or more is not abundant, and is typified by small colonies of low, encrusting corals. Deep-dwelling corals are well-represented and include several rare species such as *Leptoseris tubulifera* and *Coscinaraea wellsi*.

Also found, in addition to the hard corals, *Scleractinia*, are species of flexible black corals, *Antipatharia*. Their lack of symbiotic algae frees black corals from a need for light, but requires them to catch all their own food. At depth, black corals need not compete so heavily with stony corals for substrate, and are further benefitted by the reduction in wave action which can damage their tissues. Most black corals are finely branching forms resembling trees, with some reaching many feet in height.

Molokini's luxuriant coral growth forms the structure upon which an entire community of coral reef-related animals are dependent for both shelter and food.

Pages 46 and 47
A filefish has just taken a bite of this finger coral, *Porites compressa*. Its teeth shaved off the upper body and tentacles of some coral polyps, but left enough for the polyp to survive and eventually regenerate the lost parts.

Far left

The tiny claws of the cleaner shrimp, *Lysmata amboinesis*, are adept at picking parasites. Often found in the same place every day, cleaner shrimp attract fishes and eels, like this undulated moray, *Gymnothorax undulatus*, with their distinct coloration and the swaying movement of a pair of white legs at the front of the body.

Above

The ornate wrasse, *Halichoeres ornatissimus*, appears metallic under a strong light. This common fish feeds on small mollusks and crustaceans it catches among the coral rubble where it lives.

Left

The endemic Ewa blenny, *Plagiotremus ewaensis*, feeds on the mucus, epidermal tissue and sometimes scales of larger passing fishes by darting out and biting them. The victim often reacts sharply as did an enraged parrotfish which repeatedly charged the spot where the culprit had taken cover. Smaller fishes living nearby actually benefit from the little pest, however, since many predators learn to recognize and avoid this blenny.

Above
The striking color pattern on the head of the male psyche-
delic wrasse, *Anampses chrysocephalus*, easily distin-
guishes it from the black and white females, usually in
groups accompanied by a single male.

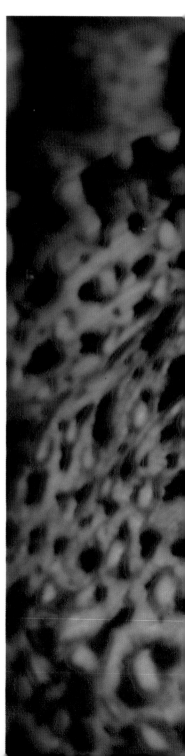

Left

The endemic Hawaiian whitespotted toby, *Canthigaster jactator*, is the most common puffer in shallow water. Puffers have a remarkable capacity to inflate their bodies with water when threatened or attacked.

Below

The dragon moray, *Enchelycore pardalis*, is among the most striking of all eels. Its "horns" are actually nostrils, which aid in locating prey. Water is drawn in through the short front pair, moved over olfactory tissue, then expelled through the tall nostrils above the eyes.

Above

A symbiotic relationship exists between *Pocillapora* corals and *Trapezia* crabs. The crabs defend the coral by pinching and pushing away any attackers, while finding shelter among the coral's branches. This female *Trapezia cymodoce maculata* is carrying hundreds of eggs.

At Right

This white dot nudibranch, a species of *Hypselodoris*, lacks a full scientific name. Despite its delicate appearance it has glands under the mantle edge that produce caustic chemicals discouraging to predators.

Left

Found only in Hawaii, Potter's angelfish, *Centropyge potteri*, is a territorial species, often living in a group consisting of a dominant male and several females. A distinguishing feature of angelfishes is the spine protruding from the bottom of the gill plate.

Below

The comblike mouth of the shortbodied blenny, *Exallias brevis*, is adapted for "raking" coral polyps which are its only food. This male is guarding several egg patches of different colors, indicating that the eggs were laid at different times, possibly by different females. The bright yellow eggs were the most recently laid.

Below
Quick and skittish, the marbled shrimp, *Spirontocaris marmorata*, is just a blur as it propels itself backward with its thick muscular tail. The long, formidable-appearing claws of the male are actually weak and useless for defense, and are sometimes discarded during escape from an attacker.

Above

The arc-eyed hawkfish, *Parracirrhites arcatus*, ordinarily favors shallow water, but has been recorded as deep as 1,000 feet. It feeds on small fishes, crabs and, less frequently, on fish eggs.

Above
Although the fourline wrasse, *Pseudocheilinus tetrataenia*, is quite common at Molokini, its territory is small and intricate and it exposes itself only briefly.

Left

The ringtail wrasse, *Cheilinus unifasciatus*, is among the largest and most aggressive of the family in Hawaii. We once watched a juvenile ringtail wrasse attack and eat a young long-spine sea urchin. Successful, it swam away with a few sea urchin spines protruding from its snout.

Above

This redbar hawkfish, *Cirrhitops fasciatus*, is lying in wait for small fishes or shrimps to come within range. The thickened lower pectoral rays of all hawkfishes may be wedged into the substrate for support, allowing them to remain motionless until they strike.

Right

The long, slender body of the variegated lizardfish, *Synodus variegatus*, and needle-sharp teeth are characteristic of this bottom-dwelling family. All feed primarily on small fishes.

Above
The sailfin tang *Zebrasoma veliferum*, is difficult to photograph anywhere except Molokini, where it is accustomed to people. This tang is a grazer on shallow water algae. When it spreads its dorsal and anal fins it almost doubles in size.

Artistically colored harlequin shrimp, *Hymenocera picta*, are generally encountered in pairs, sometimes for years in the same place, and often with the remains of a small *Linckia* starfish they have subdued and pulled to a safe place to eat.

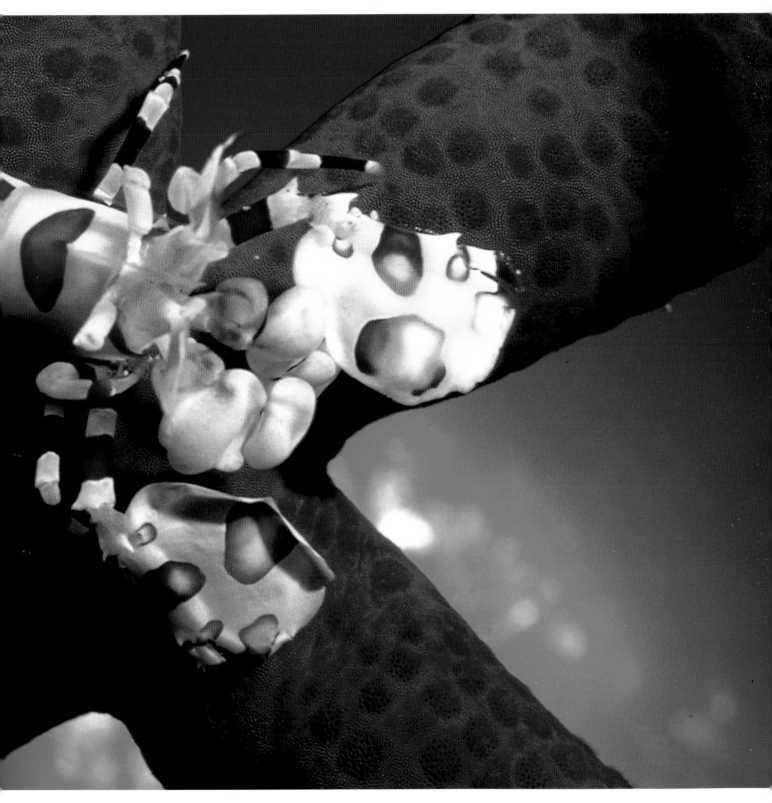

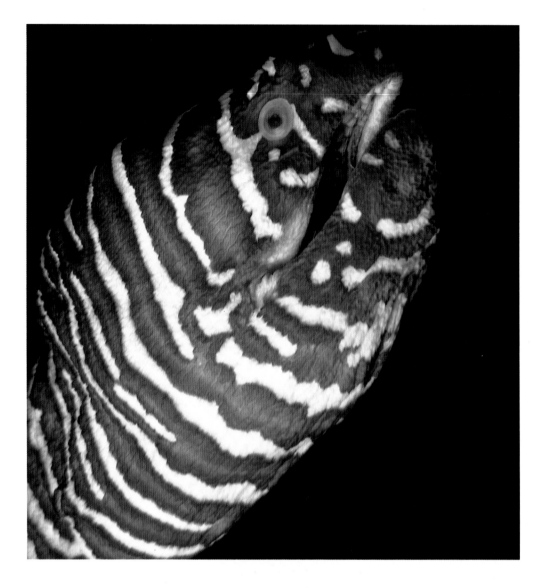

Above
The sluggish zebra moray, *Gymnomuraena zebra*, crushes crabs and bivalves with its peg-like teeth.

Right
The lack of a high gloss shell makes the endemic granulated cowry, *Cypraea granulata*, unique among cowries. The mantle, bearing long branching papillae (soft projections), provides excellent camouflage.

Above

The undersides of the pectoral fins of the devil scorpionfish, *Scorpaenopsis diabolus*, are brilliant with reds and yellows, in marked contrast to the rest of its body which resembles the bottom. The striking colors are displayed as a warning to would-be predators that it is poisonous.

Right

The spaghetti worm, *Loimia medusa*, feeds by transporting organic particles and detritus to the mouth in a "conveyor belt" manner along its outstretched tentacles.

Above
This lionfish, *Dendrochirus barberi*, is known only from the Hawaiian Islands. Although smaller than the lionfishes of the South Pacific, its defenses are equally venomous.

Left
These two male star-eye parrotfish, *Calotomus carolinus*, repeatedly charged each other, grappling mouth-to-mouth in what may have been a territorial dispute.

Above

The spectacular male belted wrasse, *Stethojulis balteata*, is usually accompanied by at least one duller gray-green female and is found only in Hawaii. Its prey which include small mollusks, worms, crustaceans and foraminifera, are usually swallowed whole.

Above
Of the lobsters found in the Hawaiian Islands, only a few small, ornate creatures possess claws. The hairy lobster, *Enoplometopus occidentalis*, emerges at night to search for algae and organic debris.

Left Above
The crown-of-thorns starfish, *Acanthaster planci* feeds on corals by extruding its stomach and secreting digestive juices that dissolve the coral polyps, often killing the entire colony.

Left
Living among the venomous spines and fuzzy respiratory papillae of the crown-of-thorns starfish is the shrimp *Periclimenes soror* which spends its entire adult life on the giant starfish.

Right

A long filament extends back from the dorsal fin of *Chaetodon auriga*, hence its popular name, the threadfin butterflyfish. Unlike others of the genus that feed exclusively on coral polyps, *C. auriga*'s ability to eat algae and polychaete worms enables it to seek food away from living coral areas.

Below

Unlike most other endemic fishes of Hawaii, the bluestripe butterflyfish, *Chaetodon fremblii*, has not been traced to any living ancestral form outside Hawaii. It may be a relic of a once wide-spread species that flourished in Hawaii while becoming extinct elsewhere.

Above Right

The orange and white pattern of the juvenile yellowtail wrasse, *Coris gaimard*, is more like that of a clownfish than of a wrasse.

Right

As it matures, colors begin to change from the tail forward. The adult has no white, the yellow tail is distinct and it is speckled with bright blue.

Above

This *Montipora capitata* coral is overcoming a colony of finger coral, *Porites compressa*. Colonies of *M. capitata* cover a reef in a thin veneer, often supported by columns of finger coral overwhelmed during its spread. When damaged, the underlying finger coral columns can be clearly seen (**at right**).

Above

The damselfish *Chromis leucura* is easily recognizable by its white tail and yellow pelvic fins, but until recently few specimens of this rare fish had been seen. It is not uncommon at Molokini.

Left

The oval butterflyfish, *Chaetodon trifasciatus*, almost always travel in pairs, feeding on coral polyps. Like many butterflyfishes, they will defend their home range against others of their species.

Above
About half the purple coral polyps of this *Montipora patula* are extended for feeding. Since all the polyps are connected, they benefit equally from the food captured by the active members of the colony.

Left
The barred filefish, *Cantherhines dumerilii*, often inverts itself to feed on coral polyps.

Right
The Christmas tree worm, *Spirobranchus giganteus*, lives in a tube surrounded by lobe coral, *Porites lobata*. Protruding from the tube is a pair of branchiae (spiral gills) and the operculum (calcareous trap door) that snaps closed when the worm is startled.

The male (**top**) and the female (**bottom**) Whitley's trunkfish, *Ostracion whitleyi*, differ so much in appearance that until 1968 the two color forms were considered separate species.

Left
The snowflake coral, *Telesto riisei*, blossoms in the current to feed as a millet seed butterflyfish passes by.

Top
The day octopus, *Octopus cyanea*, is a master of camouflage. When first approached, this octopus had a rough surface and colors which matched the bottom.

Bottom
It then quickly changed to dark brown with a pure white stripe before slipping away.

Above

While lying in wait for small fishes and crustaceans, the leaf scorpionfish, *Taenianotus triacanthus*, sometimes sways back and forth like a leaf in the surge, further enhancing its camouflage. It is not known to be poisonous.

Above
With its stout teeth the snowflake moray, *Echidna nebulosa*, crushes crabs and other crustaceans, but it has also been known to catch and eat sleeping fishes.

Right
This female redlip parrotfish, *Scarus rubroviolaceus* shows clearly the hard beak that gives the parrotfishes their popular name. Although parrotfishes actually feed on algae, the hard beak often scrapes the dead coral skeleton or rock beneath it. These flakes, consumed with the algae, account for the fish's white sandy excretion.

Above
These adult frogfish, *Antennatus tuberosus*, are barely two inches in length. Patient hunters, they sit motionless until a fish swims within striking distance. The illicium, a modified fin spine dangling in front of the head, often lures small fishes within range. In this photo it can be seen as an orange spine laid down against the forehead of the fish.

Above
Common and easily approached, the yellow tang, *Zebrasoma flavescens*, is frequently seen grazing on algae among coral and rubble. A white bar on the fish's side, normally visible only at night, can be seen in this day-time photo under the intense light of the camera strobe.

Both *Ichthyophis bennettii* (top) and the tiger moray, *Uropterygius tigrinus* (bottom), are rare eels. With long, muscular, finless bodies and sharp canine teeth, these morays rely more on scent than sight to find their prey, which consists mainly of fishes.

Right
The endemic flame wrasse, *Cirrhilabrus jordani*, hovers in colonies feeding on drifting zooplankton. The male (figured here) usually keeps several females in a well-defined territory. When one strays too far the male, displaying his full colors, chases it back.

Top

Schools of the endemic chocolate-dip damsel, *Chromis hanui*, swim a couple feet off the bottom, feeding on drifting zoo-plankton. When frightened in their constant feeding, they dive for cover en masse.

Bottom

The Pacific gregory, *Stegastes fasciolatus*, grazes on filamentous algae it cultivates within its well-defended territory. Able to recognize grazing fish that threaten its cultured food supply, it chases them off while allowing non-grazers to pass undisturbed. This damselfish weeds "undesirable" algae from its territory by pulling them with its mouth.

Above
The longnose butterflyfish, *Forcipiger flavissimus*, feeds primarily on tube worms, but may also nibble the tube feet of sea urchins and the cirri (thin feeding appendages) of barnacles. This habit of picking away at the exposed organs of bottom-dwelling animals is well-suited to its long snout.

Right
The eggs of the endemic Hawaiian damselfish, *Dascyllus albisella*, are laid on smooth rock and dead coral surfaces, and aggressively guarded by the male. In this photograph, the darker male is fertilizing the eggs as the lighter female deposits them.

Above

This metallic-appearing leatherback, *Scomberoides lysan*, a member of the jack fish family, is being cleaned of parasites by a Hawaiian cleaner wrasse, *Labroides phthirophagus*, whose Latin name means louse eater.

Below
This night photo of a bullethead parrotfish, *Scarus sordidus*, shows the characteristic pose of sleeping parrotfishes. Some species, such as the bullethead, secrete a cocoon of mucous around themselves, which may conceal them from predators.

Above at right inset

Stalking a Hawaiian damselfish, *Dascyllus albisella*, a yellow trumpetfish, *Aulostomus chinensis*, is taking advantage of the confusion created by so many fishes together at once.

Right insets

The attack was successful and the outline of the damselfish can be seen within the trumpetfish's snout. The trumpetfish usually swallows its prey head-first, expanding its gill covers and pushing its gills out of the way as the fish passes down the throat.

Right

The prey is visible as a lump until it is digested.

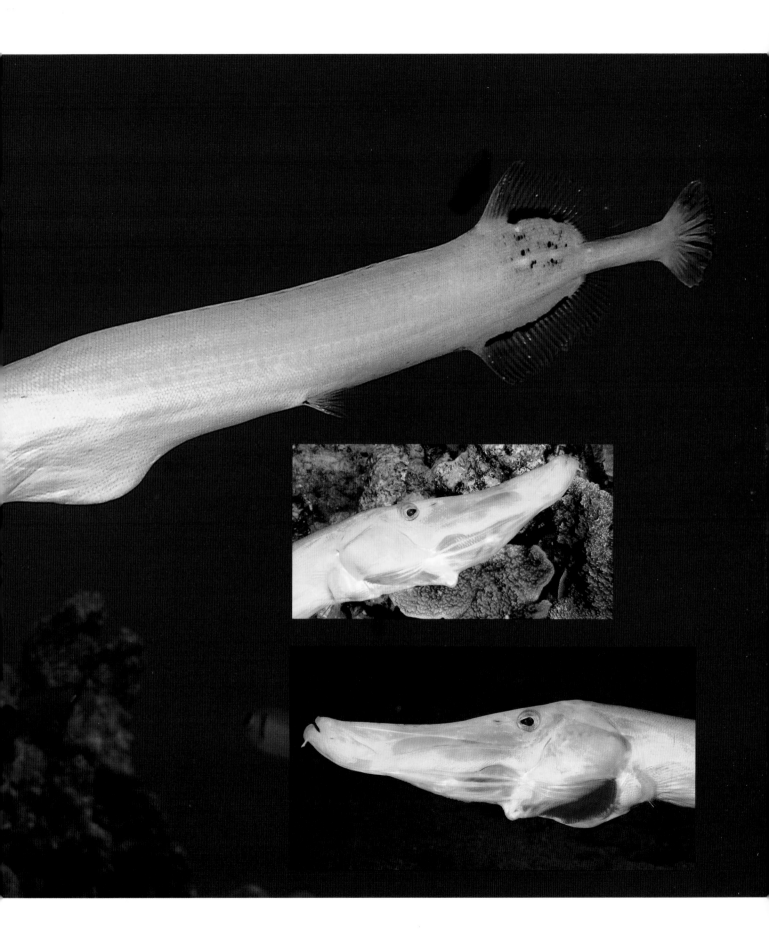

OUTER WALL

OUTER WALL

Seaward of Molokini's crescent, contrasting sharply with its relatively shallow, protected bay, are the dramatic drop-offs and sloping ledges of the island's outer walls. Here, at the interface of island and pelagic sea, the wall is nearly vertical and at its base meets with sand bottom at depths ranging from 250 to 300 feet. Where severe erosion of the island has occurred, accumulated rocks and rubble at the base of the island may extend upward to a depth of 180 feet.

Approaching the foot of the wall from the relatively flat sand bottom which surrounds the island, the first major feature encountered is an ancient undercut shoreline at 250 feet which still bears the scars of sea urchins that once hollowed out cavities in the rock. Similar urchins can be seen today in their stone burrows in the shallow intertidal and surge zone along the island's coast and attest to the once shallow habitat that existed at the base of the wall when sea level was considerably lower.

At these depths there are only a few small species of hard corals, tree-like black corals, and the soft, white octocoral *Telesto riisei*. The surface of the wall is covered with yellow, red, and green encrusting sponges, green algae and purple coraline algae. Beneath ledges and in caves dense colonies of the cup coral *Tubastraea coccinea* thrive. Ascending the wall above 200 feet, there are progressively more species of corals, most noticeably the deep water variety of the common rose coral, *Pocilopora meandrina*. Nearing the surface, coral and fish species increase dramatically, until there is a virtual explosion of life in the surge zone.

Few species of fish live below 200 feet but surprisingly several fish species at this depth, such as the moorish idol and the long-nosed butterflyfish, are common in shallow water. Of the fishes that live exclusively on the lower wall, probably the best-known is Tinker's butterflyfish, *Chaetodon tinkeri*.

Currents striking Molokini increase in speed as they are forced around the island. These fast-moving tidal currents wash the outer wall with nutrient-rich water providing food for thousands of animals. Schools of butterflyfishes, surgeonfishes, damselfishes and triggerfishes feed on zooplankton while hovering in the currents, but remain within reach of the shelter provided by the island. Corals, tunicates and sponges all thrive in the strong current which not only brings food, but sweeps away silt and debris that may inhibit their growth.

Cracks and fissures in the rock provide deep, dark and narrow hiding places for many nocturnal residents, but not all of these cracks are hospitable all of the time. Periodically rainwater, heated while percolating down through the sun-warmed island above, accumulates in the vertical cracks along the wall. Eventually the warm freshwater seeps completely from these cracks into the sea, restoring favorable conditions.

The colors of the outer wall create a stunning contrast to the deep blue of the surrounding ocean. Against this backdrop schools of silver mackeral scad and needlefish travel along the wall in search of their microscopic food. Big game fishes such as ono, mahimahi, and jacks often accompany the schools looking for an opportunity to feed on the tightly-packed schools and can be seen close to the wall as they trail their prey.

Very little about the outer wall is duplicated anywhere else in the crater. Large rarely-seen pelagic animals slide quietly into view and leave just as quietly. These giants of the sea leave no sign of their passing, while up from the depths come fish so rare that almost nothing is known of their habits. The outer wall is unique, bringing many animals from distinctly different habitats together in one place.

Above left
Living in clumps of *Caulerpa* algae, the green bubble shell, *Lobiger souverbiei*, punctures the algal sacks and sucks out their contents, retaining the chloroplasts which account for its brilliant green color.

Pages 92 and 93
Beneath overhangs along the back wall are colonies of the bright orange cup coral, Tubastraea coccinea, that, particularly at night, open their tentacles to capture zooplankton.

Top
The deep-dwelling yellowfin soldierfish, *Myripristis chryseres*, may mix with the whitetip soldierfish, *Myripristis vittata*, (bottom) a fish not known from Hawaii prior to its discovery at Molokini by the authors.

Above
The normally five-armed blood-spotted starfish, *Linckia
multifora*, is a favorite prey of the harlequin shrimp,
Hymenocera picta. When attacked it will often abandon an
arm and escape, eventually regenerating the missing arm.

Above

The dorsal spines of the endemic turkeyfish, *Pterois sphex*, can inflict a painful sting. When displaying its fins in a warning posture, it will scull along with its tail. If the warning is not heeded, however, the display instantly collapses and the turkeyfish darts to safety.

Left
An old black coral tree covered with sponges provides a colorful habitat for many fishes including a rose-colored frog fish perched among the branches.

Above
The male fairy anthias, *Pseudanthias ventralis hawaiiensis*, usually swims upside-down with a group of slightly less colorful females beneath ledges deeper than 130 feet. Its varied diet includes fish eggs, copepods and crustacean larvae.

Left
The slate pencil urchin, *Heterocentrotus mammillatus*, thrives in the shallows where it anchors itself to graze on algae and debris. The red protein coat protects the spines from fouling. A tiny red shrimp sometimes lives among the spines.

Bottom left
This nudibranch, *Tambja morosa,* is laying its bright orange eggs. Encapsulated and surrounded by mucus, they will adhere to the rock until they hatch.

Right
The endemic darkfin bass, *Holanthias fuscipinnis*, normally lives at depths greater than 400 feet. Prior to this photograph taken at 200 feet, this fish had been seen only through the viewing ports of research submersibles.

Above

The large eyes and preference for dark crevices of the deep-water long-handed lobster, *Justitia longimana*, indicate it is a nocturnal feeder. Unlike Hawaii's other spiny lobsters, its front pair of appendages is highly modified for feeding, being more robust than its walking legs and possessing strong hooked claws at the ends.

Left

The shallow-water leviathan cowry, *Cypraea leviathan*, found only in Hawaii, emerges in the surge zone at night to feed on sponges and organic debris. The eyes are visible at the base of the tentacles.

Above

The food of this undescribed species of *Phidiana*, includes coelenterates, whose stinging nematocyst cells it stores in the projections on its back. To the right, a tiny squat lobster, a species of *Galathea,* is emerging from its hole.

Above
Extremely rare, this undescribed species of *Hypselodoris* is so far known only from Hawaii. It feeds on sponges at depths of over 100 feet along the back wall.

Above
The very small *Harpilius depressus* shrimp lives on the long furry stalk of the snake wire coral, *Cirrhipathes anguina*, blending with its color and texture. It cleans the coral of parasites; the coral in return provides a place to live.

Above
The endemic Achilles tang, *Acanthurus achilles*, feeds along the outer wall, snatching at algae in the turbulent surge zone. The bright orange spot near the tail may be a warning to predators that a very sharp spine near its tail can inflict quick, deep cuts in other fishes.

Left
This orange *Dromidiopsis* sponge crab commonly holds a piece of sponge across its back for protection. This one, instead, has picked up a small starfish that is arching back and feeling about with its tube feet.

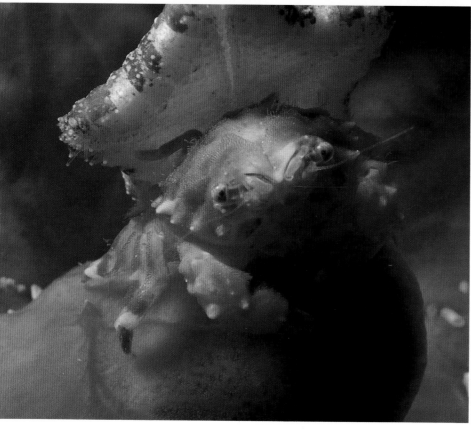

Above
A filterfeeder, the large and conspicuous featherduster worm, *Sebellastarte sanctijosephi*, builds a tough, flexible tube that is anchored among rock and coral.

Left
Primarily a night feeder, the whitetip reef shark, *Triaenodon obesus*, rests under ledges during the day. It preys on sleeping fishes such as parrotfishes, which it locates with electrosensory and chemosensory organs on its head.

Below
The gray reef shark, *Carcharhinus amblyrhynchus*, frequents the deeper water of Molokini's outer wall. A fast, powerful swimmer, it is most active at night.

Above
Because of its size the hairy hermit crab, *Aniculus maximus*, usually seeks the shell of a partridge tun, *Tonna perdix*, pictured here, or a triton's trumpet, *Charonia tritonis*.

Above

Many animals spend their lives drifting in ocean currents, and a generous sampling comes to Molokini. Among these is this jellyfish which feeds primarily on pelagic crustaceans.

Right

The membrane between the dorsal spines of the decoy scorpionfish, *Iracundus signifer*, resembles a small fish. If a curious predator comes near, *I. signifer* strikes and the would-be predator becomes prey.

Above
This pelagic *Hippocampus* seahorse drifts among debris at the ocean's
surface. It occasionally drifts past Molokini.

Above Left
The endemic Hawaiian sergeant, *Abudefduf abdominalis*, lays its eggs on a patch of bottom it has cleared of debris. The eggs will become paler as they mature while being guarded by one or sometimes both parents.

Below Left
Closely resembling the Hawaiian sergeant *Abudefduf abdominalis*, this sergeant major, *Abudefduf zaigiensis*, is a recent arrival at Molokini and the first of its kind recorded in the Hawaiian Islands. The injury on its tail occurred while it was guarding its eggs.

Above
The stunning flame angelfish, *Centropyge loriculus*, exhibits the brightest coloration of its Indo-Pacific range in Hawaii.

Above
This hermit crab has taken up residence in one of the most substantial shells on the reef, the open dye shell, *Purpura aperta*. The advantage of such a large shell is that it leaves room for growth; the disadvantage is that it may present a mobility problem.

Above
The small-mouth squirrelfish, *Sargocentron ensiferum,* found in deep water, usually in association with soldier-fishes during the day, is most active at night when it feeds primarily on crustaceans, worms and small fishes.

Right
A pair of Yonge's gobies, *Bryaninops yongei,* sit on a stalk of spiral wire coral, *Cirrhipathes spiralis,* which the gobies will occupy for life.

Above

This frogfish, *Antennarius commersoni*, matches the brilliant red encrusting sponge *Dimiriana hawaiiana*. Frogfishes often change color, but the process usually takes several weeks. For this reason they remain in one place for long periods.

Left Above

The red pipefish, *Dunkerocampus baldwini,* is closely related to the seahorses and feeds on minute organisms by quickly sucking water into its tiny tubular mouth.

Left Below

The endemic bandit angelfish, *Holocanthus arcatus*, generally swims in pairs along the bottom in search of the sponges that constitute much of its diet. The largest Hawaiian angelfish, it is territorial and can be found in the same area day after day.

Above

The stenopid shrimps have five pairs of "legs," the first three possessing pinchers. The first two pairs, quite small, are for grooming and feeding, while the massive third pair is mainly for territorial displays and defense. It uses the remaining pairs, long and spread out, to move and to give the shrimp a stable stance. The largest of Hawaii's stenopid shrimps, the fountain shrimp, *Stenopus pyrsonotus*, has a claw span up to eight inches. Pairs live in crevices usually below 100 feet.

Above
Bicolor anthias, *Pseudanthias bicolor,* can be found in large aggregations over large deep-water coral heads. When approached, the members crowd into small openings in the reef, peering out until the danger has passed.

Above

The endemic titan scorpionfish, *Scorpaenopsis cacopsis*, is Hawaii's largest and most ornate. It can be two feet long and weigh several pounds. A carnivore, it has even been noted to eat small trumpetfish.

Above
The red-legged swimming crab, *Charybdis erythrodactyla*, defends itself with sharp claws. A night feeder, it spends its days in crevices.

Above
The raccoon butterflyfish, *Chaetodon lunula*, is the only nocturnal butterflyfish reported so far from Molokini. Pairs often hide under shaded ledges in the daytime. At other times they move about the deeper reef in schools of 30 or 40, feeding on a variety of invertebrates.

Below
Tinker's butterflyfish, *Chaetodon tinkeri*, is among the rarest of the butterflyfishes in Hawaii. Its range extends to depths greater than 600 feet where it has been recorded by research submarines. When encountered it is a remarkably curious fish.

Left
This goby, *Pleurosicya micheli*, was found living on a colony of the plate coral, *Leptoseris hawaiiensis*, at 280 feet on the back wall of the island — a new depth record for this species.

Above

The gilded triggerfish, *Xanthichthys auro-marginatus*, swims high off the sea bottom in strong currents to capture tiny copepods and other zooplankton. These fish school for breeding in the early summer, laying eggs in sand and rubble patches which the female guards.

Left

This adult dwarf moray, *Gymnothorax melatremus*, is only about ten inches long. Little is known of its habits since it remains among the small rubble and deep in cracks.

Above

The redtail triggerfish, *Xanthichthys mento*, (a male is figured) lives along the northern slope of Molokini and feeds on zooplankton. Normally remaining at about 300 feet, it rises to as shallow as 130 feet in summer.

Above

The mackerel scad, *Decapterus pinnulatus*, moves through the crater and along the outer wall in large schools, feeding on zooplankton. Predators work in teams to concentrate the fish, then charge the tightly packed school.

Left

The reticulated butterflyfish, *Chaetodon reticulatus*, usually lives in pairs within an established territory. We have seen this fish feed on the tentacles of the snake wire coral, *Cirrhipathes anguina*. It is also known to feed on algae.

Above
With its big, dark eyes and bearded chin, the boarfish, *Evistias acutirostris*, is one of Hawaii's most unusual fishes. During the day it stays in the dimly lit depths along the outer slopes, but at night it moves up into shallow water to feed on brittle starfishes.

Above
The endemic milletseed butterflyfish, *Chaetodon miliaris*, is often in loose schools feeding on zooplankton. These fish will overwhelm a male damselfish guarding a nest, forming bright, rapidly feeding clusters as the entire school descends on the eggs.

Above left
This rare *Phyllidia* species resembles another common nudibranch, *Phyllidia varicosa*. Like all Phyllidia, it secretes a foul-tasting substance when attacked.

Left
The longnose hawkfish, *Oxycirrhites typus*, often lives among the branches of black coral which slow crustaceans and small organisms sweeping by, making capture easier for the fish.

Top

This formation of shoulderbar soldierfish, *Myripristis kuntee*, suggests the origin of the group's common name. It is a homogenous school except for two brick soldierfish, *M. amaena*, lacking the shoulderbar. At night this school will disperse to feed, coming together again in the morning. In the background, is a large yellowmargin moray, *Gymnothorax flavimarginatus*.

Bottom

The endemic masked angelfish, *Genicanthus personatus*, is rarely seen because it lives in very deep water. This female was photographed at 300 feet where it had ventured up from the bottom to feed in the water column.

Above

The distinguishing feature of squirrelfishes, a spine projecting from the gill plate, is most visible on *Sargocentron spiniferum*, the sabre squirrelfish. Venomous in some species, the spine is used for defense.

Above

The endemic spiny lobster, *Panulirus marginatus,* is one of three species of large spiny lobsters found in Hawaii. This female is carrying orange eggs which she is aerating by gently flapping her tail and by agitating them with one of her legs.

Left

A juvenile medusa fish clings to a jellyfish, *Cephea cephea,* as its only shelter in the open ocean. At this size it is able to dive inside the bell of the jellyfish if a predator nears. However, as an adult it will have to find a larger host, such as a floating log, for protection.

MOLOKINI ISLAND

FIG. 1

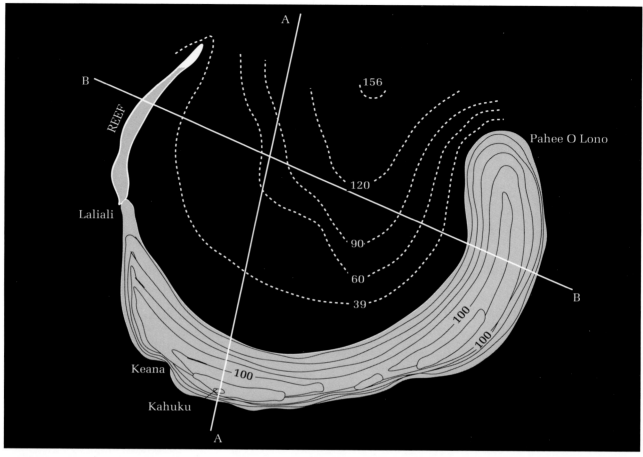

FIG. 2

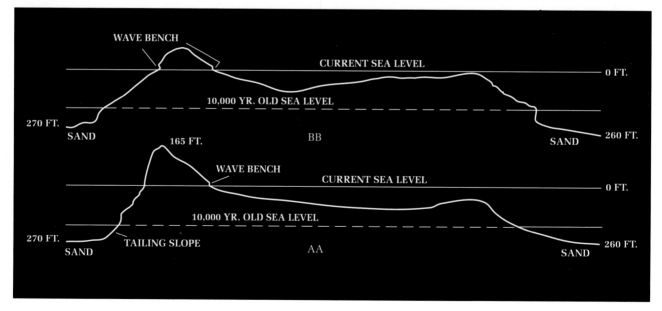

Fig. 1: **Molokini Island**. After Harold S. Palmer Oct. 1925. Land contour interval = 20 feet
.... Submarine contour lines in feet. 1 in. = 140 ft.

Fig. 2: These cross sections show Molokini as a volcanic cone on a relatively flat sea floor. They were produced using SCUBA by recording the depth at ten foot intervals along compass bearings indicated by lines AA and BB in Fig. 1. The current preserve boundary is indicated by the 180 foot depth line.

HAWAII'S MARINE LIFE CONSERVATION DISTRICTS

Molokini is one of nine Marine Life Conservation Districts (MLCDs) in Hawai'i. Designated by the state's Department of Natural Resources, MLCDs are intended to conserve and replenish Hawai'i's marine resources. Some MLCDs, like Hanauma Bay on Oahu, prohibit boats and fishing of any kind. Others, like Molokini, allow boats and limited fishing. They are all intended to provide marine life with a protected area and at the same time provide access to people who wish to observe Hawai'i's beautiful marine fauna. Because the animals in MLCDs are protected and because they are accustomed to the presence of divers and snorkelers, MLCDs are often the best areas to get close to fish and to photograph them.

Below is a list of the current MLCDs in Hawai'i. While rules for each MLCD differ, it is generally prohibited to take any living material or non-living habitat material (rocks, sand, coral skeletons). To avoid confusion it is probably best to avoid any consumptive activities within the protected area. Complete rules are available from the Division of Aquatic Resources, 1151 Punchbowl Street, Room 330, Honolulu, HI 96813.

MAUI
Molokini Shoal
Honolua-Mokuleia Bay

OAHU
Hanauma Bay
Pupukea
Waikiki

HAWAII
Kealakekua Bay
Lapakahi
Waialea Bay

LANAI
Manele-Hulopoe

At right:
This manta ray, *Manta alfredi*, identified by the unique pattern of spots on its underside, has been sighted and photographed at Molokini several times over the past five years. Photo by Dave B. Fleetham.

FISH SPECIES RECORDED FROM MOLOKINI
1985-1992

Family Rhincodontidae (Whale Sharks)

Rhincodon typus

Family Carcharhinidae (Requiem Sharks)

Carcharhinus amblyrhynchos

Carcharhinus melanopterus

Galeocerdo cuvier

Family Hemigaleidae (Weasel Sharks)

Triaenodon obesus

Family Sphyrnidae (Hammerhead Sharks)

Sphyrna sp.

Family Myliobatidae (Eagle Rays)

Aetobatus narinari

Family Mobulidae (Manta Rays)

Manta alfredi

Family Muraenidae (Morays)

Echidna nebulosa

Enchelycore pardalis

Enchelynassa canina

Gymnothorax eurostus

Gymnothorax flavimarginatus

Gymnothorax gracilicaudus

Gymnothorax melatremus

Gymnothorax meleagris

Gymnothorax undulatus

Gymnomuraena zebra

Scuticaria bennetti

Scuticaria tigrinus

Family Ophichthidae (Snake Eels)

Brachysomophis henshawi

Callechelys luteus

Family Congridae (Conger Eels)

Conger Cinereus

Gorgasia hawaiiensis

Poeciloconger fasciatus

Family Engraulidae (Anchovy Fishes)

Stolephorus sp.

Family Synodontidae (Lizardfishes)

Saurida flamma

Synodus binotatus

Synodus lobeli

Synodus variegatus

Family Brotulidae (Brotulas)

Brotula multibarbata

Family Antennariidae (Frogfishes)

Antennarius commersoni

Antennatus tuberosus

Histrio histrio

Family Belonidae (Needlefishes)

Ablennes hians

Tylosurus crocodilus

Family Holocentridae (Squirrelfishes and Soldierfishes)

Myripristis amaena

Myripristis berndti

Myripristis chryseres

Myripristis kuntee

Myripristis vittata

Neoniphon aurolineatus

Plectrypops lima

Sargocentron ensiferum

Sargocentron spiniferum

Sargocentron tiere

Sargocentron xantherythrum

Family Aulostomidae (Trumpetfishes)

Aulostomus chinensis

Family Fistulariidae (Flutemouths)

Fistularia commersonii

Family Syngnathidae (Pipefishes)

Doryhamphus excisus

Dunckerocampus baldwini

Family Dactylopteridae (Flying Gurnards)

Dactyloptena orientalis

Family Scorpaenidae (Scorpionfishes)

Dendrochirus barberi

Iracundus signifer

Pterois sphex

Scorpaenopsis diabolus

Scorpaenopsis cacopsis

Sebastapistes coniorta

Taenianotus triacanthus

Family Caracanthidae (Velvetfishes)

Caracanthus typicus

Family Serranidae (Groupers)

Cephalopholis argus

Epinephelus lanceolatus

Holanthias elizabethae

Holanthias fuscipinnis

Liopropoma aurora

Pseudanthias bicolor

Pseudanthias thompsoni

Pseudanthias ventralis hawaiiensis

Family Kuhliidae (Flagtails)

Kuhlia sandvicensis

Family Priacanthidae (Bigeyes)

Heteropriacanthus cruentatus

Heteropriacanthus meeki

Family Apogonidae (Cardinalfishes)

Apogon kallopterus

Apogon taeniopterus

Family Malacanthidae (Sand Tilefishes)

Malacanthus brevirostris

Family Carangidae (Trevallies)

Alectis indica

Carangoides ferdau

Caranx ignobilis

Caranx melampygus

Caranx sexfasciatus

Decapterus pinnulatus

Elagatis bipinnulata

Scomberoides lysan

Selar crumenophthalmus

Seriola rivoliana

Family Nomeidae (Driftfishes)

Psenes arafuraensis

Family Lutjanidae (Snappers)

Aphareus furca

Aprion virescens

Lutjanus fulvus

Lutjanus kasmira

Family Lethrinidae (Emperors)

Monotaxis grandoculis

Family Mullidae (Goatfishes)

Mulloidichthys flavolineatus

Mulloidichthys pflugeri

Mulloidichthys vanicolensis

Parupeneus bifasciatus

Parupeneus cyclostomus

Parupeneus multifasciatus

Parupeneus pleurostigma

Parupeneus porphyreus

Family Kyphosidae (Sea Chubs)

Kyphosus bigibbus

Kyphosus vaigiensis

Family Pentacerotidae (Boarfishes)

Evistias acutirostris

Family Chaetodontidae (Butterflyfishes)

Chaetodon auriga

Chaetodon fremblii

Chaetodon kleinii

Chaetodon lunula

Chaetodon miliaris

Chaetodon multicinctus

Chaetodon ornatissimus

Chaetodon quadrimaculatus

Chaetodon reticulatus

Chaetodon tinkeri

Chaetodon trifascialis

Chaetodon trifasciatus

Chaetodon unimaculatus

Forcipiger flavissimus

Forcipiger longirostris

Hemitaurichthys polylepis

Hemitaurichthys thompsoni

Heniochus diphreutes

Family Pomacanthidae (Angelfishes)

Centropyge fisheri

Centropyge loriculus

Centropyge potteri

Genicanthus personatus

Holacanthus arcuatus

Family Pomacentridae (Damselfishes)

Abudefduf abdominalis

Abudefduf sordidus

Abudefduf vaigiensis

Chromis agilis

Chromis hanui

Chromis leucura

Chromis ovalis

Chromis vanderbilti

Chromis verater

Dascyllus albisella

Plectroglyphidodon johnstonianus

Plectroglyphidodon imparipennis

Stegastes fasciolatus

Family Cirrhitidae (Hawkfishes)

Amblycirrhitus bimacula

Cirrhitops fasciatus

Cirrhitus pinnulatus

Oxycirrhites typus

Paracirrhites arcatus

Paracirrhites forsteri

Family Sphyraenidae (Barracudas)

Sphyraena barracuda

Sphyraena helleri

Family Labridae (Wrasses)

Anampses chrysocephalus

Anampses cuvier

Bodianus bilunulatus

Cheilinus unifasciatus

Cheilio inermis

Cirrhilabrus jordani

Coris ballieui

Coris flavovittata

Coris gaimard

Coris venusta

Cymolutes lecluse

Gomphosus varius

Halichoeres ornatissimus

Labroides phthirophagus

Macropharyngodon geoffroy

Macropharyngodon meleagris

Novaculichthys taeniourus

Novaculops woodi

Pseudocheilinus evanidus

Pseudocheilinus octotaenia

Pseudocheilinus tetrataenia

Pseudojuloides cerasinus

Stethojulis balteata

Thalassoma ballieui

Thalassoma duperrey

Thalassoma lutescens

Thalassoma purpureum

Thalassoma quinquevittatum

Thalassoma trilobatum

Xyrichtys aneitensis

Xyrichtys niger

Xyrichtys pavo

Family Scaridae (Parrotfishes)

Calotomus carolinus

Carolinus zonarchus

Scarus dubius

Scarus perspicillatus

Scarus psittacus

Scarus rubroviolaceus

Scarus sordidus

Family Pinguipedidae (Sandperches)

Parapercis schauinslandi

Family Blenniidae (Blennies)

Cirripectes obscurus

Cirripectes vanderbilti

Entomacrodus marmoratus

Exallias brevis

Plagiotremus ewaensis

Plagiotremus goslinei

Family Callionymidae (Dragonets)

Callionymus sp.

Family Gobiidae (Gobies)

Bryaninops yongei

Pleurosicya micheli

Pleurosicya sp.

Priolepis auroviridis

Priolepis sp.

Family Microdesmidae (Wormfishes and Dartfishes)

Nemateleotris magnifica

Ptereleotris heteroptera

Family Acanthuridae (Surgeonfishes)

Acanthurus achilles

Acanthurus blochii

Acanthurus dussumieri

Acanthurus guttatus

Acanthurus leucopareius

Acanthurus nigricans

Acanthurus nigrofuscus

Acanthurus nigroris

Acanthurus olivaceus

Acanthurus triostegus

Acanthurus xanthopterus

Ctenochaetus hawaiiensis

Ctenochaetus strigosus

Naso annulatus

Naso brevirostris

Naso caesium

Naso hexacanthus

Naso lituratus

Naso maculatus

Naso unicornis

Zebrasoma flavescens

Zebrasoma veliferum

Family Zanclidae (Moorish Idol)

Zanclus cornutus

Family Scombridae (Tunas and Mackerels)

Acanthocybium solandri

Euthynnus affinus

Neothunnus albacares

Family Bothidae (Lefteye Flounders)

Bothus mancus

Bothus pantherinus

Family Balistidae (Triggerfishes)

Canthidermis maculatus

Melichthys niger

Melichthys vidua

Rhinecanthus rectangulus

Sufflamen bursa

Sufflamen fraenatus

Xanthichthys auromarginatus

Xanthichthys mento

Family Monacanthidae (Leatherjackets)

Aluterus scriptus

Cantherhinus dumerilii

Cantherhinus sandwichiensis

Cantherhinus verecundus

Pervagor aspricaudus

Pervagor spilosoma

Family Ostraciidae (Boxfishes)

Lactophrys diaphanus

Lactoria fornasini

Ostracion meleagris

Ostracion whitleyi

Family Tetraodontidae (Puffers)

Arothron hispidus

Arothron meleagris

Canthigaster Amboinensis

Canthigaster coronata

Canthigaster epilampra

Canthigaster jactator

Family Diodontidae (Porcupinefishes)

Diodon holocanthus

Diodon hystrix

Subclass Zoantharia

ORDER SCLERACTINIA (STONY CORALS)

Family **Pocilloporidae**

Pocillopora damicornis

Pocillopora meandrina

Pocillopora ligulata

Pocillopora eydouxi

Family **Acroporidae**

Montipora capitata

Montipora patula

Family **Agariciidae**

Pavona varians

Pavona duerdeni

Pavona maldivensis

Leptoseris incrustans

Leptoseris hawaiiensis [2]

Leptoseris mysetoseroides [1]

Leptoseris tubulifera [2]

Family **Balanophyllidae**[+]

Balanophyllia hawaiiensis

Family **Dendrophyllidae**[+]

Tubastraea coccinea

Family **Faviidae**

Cyphastrea ocellina

Leptastrea purpurea

Leptastrea bottae

Family **Fungiidae**

Fungia scutaria

Cycloseris vaughani

Family **Siderastreidae**

Coscinaraea wellsi

Family **Thamnasteridae**

Psammocora stellata

Psammocora explanulata [1*]

Family **Poritidae**

Porites compressa

Porites lobata

Porites brighami

Porites lichen

Porites evermanni

Porites rus

ORDER ANTIPATHARIA (BLACK CORALS)

Cirrhipathes anguina [3]

Cirrhipathes spiralis [3]

Antipathes intermedia [3]

Antipathes dichotoma [3]

Antipathes grandis [3]

Follows Maragos (1977) as revised in Veron (1986) nomenclature.
Based on unpublished 1989 Maragos observations except where otherwise noted.
[1] Collected by M. Severns, identified by James Maragos
[2] Identified by James Maragos from photographs taken by M. Severns
[3] Author's data
[*] New record for the Hawaiian Islands
[+]Non-reef building family

BIBLIOGRAPHY

Allen, G. R. *Damselfishes of the South Seas.* Neptune City, N. J.: THF Publications, Inc., 1975.

_____ and A. R. Emery. *A Review of the Pomacentrid Fishes of the Genus Stegastes from the Indo-Pacific. Indo-Pacific Fishes, no. 3.* Honolulu: B. P. Bishop Museum Press, 1985.

Arago, J. *Narrative of a Voyage Round the World.* London: Treuttel and Wurtz., 1823.

Ashdown, I. "The Legend of Black Coral." *Pacific Art and Travel,* Autumn, 1989.

Berger, A. J. *Hawaiian Birdlife.* Honolulu: The University Press of Hawaii, 1972.

Bertsch, H., and S. Johnson. *Hawaiian Nudibranchs.* Honolulu: Oriental Publishing Company, 1981.

Bruce, R. W., and J. E. Randall. "Revision of the Indo-Pacific Parrotfish Genera Calotomus." *Indo-Pacific Fishes, no. 5.* Honolulu: B. P. Bishop Museum Press, 1985.

Buck, P. H. "Report of the Director." *B. P. Bishop Museum Bulletin,* 1936, 149 (17).

Caum, E. L. . "Notes on the Flora of Molokini." *B. P. Bishop Museum Occasional Papers,* 1930, 9 (1).

Clarke, G. *A Botanical Reconnaissance of Molokini Island.* Hawaii Department of Land and Natural Resources, Division of Forestry, 1982.

Devaney, D. M., and L. G. Eldredge, eds.. *Reef and Shore Fauna of Hawaii. Sec. 1: Protozoa through Ctenophora.* B. P. Bishop Museum Special Publication, 1977, 64 (1).

_____. *Reef and Shore Fauna of Hawaii. Sec. 2: Platyhelminthes through Phoronida and Sec. 3: Sipuncula through Annelida.* B. P. Bishop Museum Special Publication, 1987, 64 (2,3).

Edmondson, C. H. "Hawaiian Dromiidae." *B. P. Bishop Museum Occasional Papers,* 1922, 8 (2).

_____. *Reef and Shore Fauna of Hawaii.* B. P. Bishop Museum Special Publication, 1933, 22.

_____. "Hawaiian Portunidae." *B. P. Bishop Museum Occasional Papers,* 1954, 21 (12).

_____. "Xanthidae of Hawaii." *B. P. Bishop Museum Occasional Papers,* 1962, 22 (13).

Eschmeyer, W. N., and J. E. Randall. "The Scorpaenid Fishes of the Hawaiian Islands, Including New Species and Records (Pisces: Scorpaenidae)." *Proc. of the California Academy of Sciences,* 1975. 40 (11): 265-334.

Fielding, A. *Hawaiian Reefs and Tidepools.* Honolulu: Oriental Publishing Company, 1979.

_____. *An Underwater Guide to Hawaii.* Honolulu: University of Hawaii Press, 1987.

Forbes, C. N. "Notes on the Flora of Kahoolawe and Molokini." *B. P. Bishop Museum Occasional Papers,* 1913, 5 (3).

Fornander, A. "Collection of Hawaiian Antiquities and Folk-lore." Ed. T. G. Thrum. *B. P. Bishop Museum Memoir,* 1916-1917, 4 (1). Chapters 1,2.

_____. "Collection of Hawaiian Antiquities and Folk-lore." Ed. T. G. Thrum. *B. P. Bishop Museum Memoir,* 1919, 5.

Gosline, V. A., and V. E. Brock. *Handbook of Hawaiian Fishes.* Honolulu:The University Press of Hawaii, 1976.

Gosliner, T. *Nudibranchs of South Africa.* Monterey, California: Sea Challengers, 1987.

Goy, J. W., and J. E. Randall. "Redescription of Stenopus devaneyi and Stenopus earlei from the Indo-West Pacific Region (Decapoda: Stenopodidae)." *B. P. Bishop Museum Occasional Papers,* 1986, 26:81-101.

Hobdy, R. W. *Vegetation of Molokini Islet.* Unpublished, 1982.

_____. "Portulaca molokiniensis (Portulacaceae), a New Species from the Hawaiian Islands." *Pacific Science*, 1987. 41 (1-4).

Honolulu Advertiser. "Molokini and the Mo'o Maiden." 1960, June 26, A23.

_____. "Lonely Island." June 29,1974, A11.

_____. "Aerial photograph." June 10,1975, F8.

_____. "Navy Divers." July 29, 1975, A6.

_____. "Preserve Date." July 7, 1977, A3.

_____. "The Barren Islet of Molokini." May 27,1983, A22.

_____. "Divers Move Two Bombs." June 12,1984, C2.

_____. "Molokini Blasts Rile Maalaea Charter Operations." Sept. 13, 1984, B11.

_____. "Plans for Detonation off Molokini Island." Nov. 15, 1984, A23.

_____. "Small Isle Site of Big Dispute." , Dec. 17, 1984, A1.

_____. "Maui's Molokini - One Small Island." Dec. 19,1984, A18.

Kapakapa. " Island of Molokini." *Paradise of the Pacific*, 1940, 52 (2): 1-12.

Kay, E. A. *A Natural History of the Hawaiian Islands.* Honolulu: University Press of Hawaii, 1972.

_____. "Hawaiian Marine Shells." *B. P. Bishop Museum Special Publication*, 1979, 64 (4).

Kepler, C. B. and A. K. Kepler. "The Birds of Molokini Island, Maui." *Elepaio*, 1980, 40 (11).

Kirch, P. V. *Feathered Gods and Fishhooks.* Honolulu: University of Hawaii Press, 1985.

LaPerouse, J. *Voyage Round the World.* Amsterdam: Da Capo Press, 1968.

Macdonald, B. A. *Volcanoes.* Englewood Cliffs: Prentice-Hall, Inc., 1972.

_____ and A. T. Abbott. . *Volcanoes in the Sea. The Geology of Hawaii.* Honolulu: University Press of Hawaii, 1970.

Maragos, J. E. *Order Scleractinia, Stony Corals In Reef and Shore Fauna of Hawaii*, edited by D. M. Devaney and L. G. Eldredge, 1977, 158-241. Honolulu: Bishop Museum Press.

Maui News. "Iron Light Tower." Mar. 25, A, 1911.

_____. "Gooding Field Boosting Maui's Coral Gardens." April 27, 1917, A8.

_____. "Gymnastics Found Necessary When Exploring Little Islet of Molokini." July 31, 1926, A1.

_____. "Molokini Described, Now Used as Navy Bombing Range." Sept. 15, 1945, A6.

Myers, R. F. *Micronesian Reef Fishes.* Guam: Coral Graphics, 1989.

Olson, S. L., and H. F. James. "Prodromus of the Fossil Avifauna of the Hawaiian Islands." *Smithsonian Contributions to Zoology*, 1982, no.365.

Palmer, H. S. "Geology of Molokini." *B. P. Bishop Museum Occasional Papers*, 1930, 9 (1).

Pietsch, T. W., and D. B. Grobecker. *Frogfishes of the World.* Stanford: Stanford University Press, 1987.

Pukui, M. K., and S. H. Elbert . *Hawaiian Dictionary.* Honolulu: The University Press of Hawaii, 1965.

_____, S. H. Elbert, and E. T. Mookini. *Place Names of Hawaii.* Honolulu: The University Press of Hawaii, 1974.

Randall, J. E. "The Hawaiian Trunkfishes of the Genus Ostracion." *Copeia,*1972, no. 4:756-768.

_____. "A Revision of the Indo-Pacific Angelfish Genus Genicanthus, with Descriptions of Three New Species." *Bulletin of Marine Science*, 1975, 25 (3): 393-421.

_____. "A Review of the Serranid Fish Genus Anthias of the Hawaiian Islands, with Descriptions of Two New Species." *Contributions in Science Natural History Museum of Los Angeles County*, 1975, 302:1-13.

_____. *Red Sea Reef Fishes.* London: IMMEL Publishing, 1983.

_____. *Guide to Hawaiian Reef Fishes.* Newton Square, Penn.: Harrowood Books, 1985.

_____ and S. N. Swerdloff. "A Review of the Damselfish Genus Chromis from the Hawaiian Islands, with Descriptions of Three New Species." *Pacific Science*, 1973, 27 (4): 327-349.

_____, K. Matsura, and A. Zama. "A Revision of the Triggerfish Genus Xanthichthys, with Description of a New Species." *Bulletin of Marine Science*, 1978, 28 (4): 688- 706.

_____ and A. Edwards. "A New Labrid Fish of the Genus Thalassoma from the Pitcairn Group, with a Review of Related Indo-Pacific Species." *Journal of Aquariculture and Aquatic Sciences*, 1984, 4 (2): 13-32.

_____ and D. F. Hoese. *A Revision of the Indo-Pacific Dartfishes, Genus Ptereleotris (Perciformes: Gobioidei). Indo-Pacific Fishes, no. 7.* B. P. Bishop Museum Press, 1985.

_____ and L. Taylor. *A Review of the Indo-Pacific Fishes of the Serranid Genus Liopropoma, with Descriptions of Seven New Species.Indo-Pacific Fishes,* no. 16:688-706. Honolulu: B. P. Bishop Museum Press, 1988.

_____, G. R. Allen and R. C. Steene. *Fishes of the Great Barrier Reef and Coral Sea.* Honolulu: University of Hawaii Press, 1990.

Rudman, W. B. "The Chromodorididae (Opisthobranchia: Mollusca) of the Indo-West Pacific: the Genus Glossodoris Ehrenberg (=Casella, H. & A. Adams)." *Zool. J. Linnean Society*, 1988, 93 (2): 133-185.

Stearns, H. T. *Geology of the State of Hawaii.* Palo Alto: Pacific Books,1985.

Tinker, S. W. *Pacific Crustacea.* Rutland, Vermont: Charles E. Tuttle Company, 1965.

_____. *Sharks and Rays.* Rutland, Vermont: Charles E. Tuttle Company, 1973.

_____. *Fishes of Hawaii.* Honolulu: Hawaiian Service, Inc., 1982.

Vancouver, G. *Voyage of Discovery to the North Pacific, Vol. 2.* Amsterdam: Da Capo Press, 1968.

Waples, R. S., and J. E. Randall. "A Revision of the Hawaiian Lizardfishes of the Genus Synodus, With Descriptions of Four New Species." *Pacific Science*, 1988, 42 (3-4): 178- 213.

Watson, J. S. "Feral Rabbit Populations on Pacific Islands." *Pacific Science*, 1961, 15 (4).

AFTERWORD

Molokini, isolated from the main islands, provides refuge for an unusually diverse and flourishing marine community. It is a shallow oasis in deep ocean offering unmatched opportunities to observe and study Hawaii's marine life in the wild. It is also a fragile place where one misplaced anchor can cause damage to the reef that may take years to repair.

Maui's population is expanding, and as it does Molokini will need more and better protection than it has now. First steps include an end to trolling within the crater and the installation of additional moorings. Prohibition of anchoring within the preserve is long overdue. Expansion of the current 180 foot deep preserve boundary and the placing of buoys at corners of a one square mile preserve encompassing Molokini would protect the entire island as well as a zone of deep water around it from fishing. This would allow pelagic animals to once again approach the island unharmed. It is also necessary for greater enforcement of fish and game regulations as well as increased public awareness. Molokini will take time to recover from the bombing of the 1940's, the black coral harvest of the 1950's, 60's, and early 70's and recurring anchor damage, but properly managed, it will recover.

Molokini is a preserve like no other, but it will always remain vulnerable to the whims of those who choose to exploit it. It is up to the people of Hawaii and all those who visit to protect this unique island and its marine inhabitants.